A Bucketful of Patience

Living with Dementia

Tony Hall

Any profits made by the publication and sale of this book will be given to Bristol Dementia Action Alliance (BDAA).
www.bdaa.org.uk

Bristol Books CIC, The Courtyard, Wraxall,
Wraxall Hill, Bristol, BS48 1NA

A Bucketful of Patience:
Living with Dementia

By Tony Hall

Published by Bristol Books 2023

ISBN: 9781909446380

Typesetting and cover design: Joe Burt

A CIP record of this book is available at the British Library.

It's A Long Goodbye

by unknown author

She's leaving me, little by little,
I wish she wouldn't go.
I will be there as long as she needs me
how do I let her know?
I'd like to hold on to the memories,
I'd also like to share.
But she's further away, getting further away.
And yet, she's always there.

It's a long goodbye,
and yet I believe that she can sense us.
So much time between now and then,
when it's time against us.
There are times she almost seems like herself.
Sometimes it's just a phase.
A part of the person I once knew,
and sometimes just a trace.

It's a long goodbye,
and still I don't know just what to say.
There's so much time between now and then,
because she goes away,
a long goodbye.
Tell me how do all the others do it?
There's so much time between now and then.
How do we get through it?
It's a long goodbye.

FOR BARBARA,

MY BEST FRIEND, SWEETHEART AND WIFE.

02/06/46 - 26/04/22

Preface	11
1962 – 1979: Beginnings	15
1999: Dementia Looms	20
2007: Diagnosis	27
2008: Support	33
2009: Life after Diagnosis	44
2010: The Limes	47
2011: Person Centred Care	51
2012: Olympic Year and Barbara becomes a "Hugger"	54
2013: The Launch of Bristol Dementia Action Alliance	60
2014: Is Bristol a Dementia Friendly City?	66
2015: Happy Days are Here Again	70
2016: BDAA Becomes a Registered Charity	76
2017: Recognition and Awards	81
2018: Growth	88
2019: Dementia progresses	93
2020: Covid 19 Strikes	97
2021: Eating and Drinking Problems	103
A Mini – Environment	113
Ups and Downs – Highs and Lows	121
2022: Dementia Wins	125
A Celebration of Barbara's life	135
2023: A Year of Anniversaries	142

"In life we all need a bucketful of patience at some time, and Tony has this in spades. His outlook, empathy and approach to dementia should be mirrored by all who work so hard in dealing with this disease."
Norrms McNamara, founder of the Purple Angel Dementia Campaign (Charity number 1189616)

"Caring for another human being is the ultimate privilege, but no easy task. Purple Angel believes that people living with dementia and those who care for them should be supported and respected. We can all make a difference when we fully understand dementia and awareness is key. Our thanks to everyone striving to understand how it feels to experience dementia or to be caring for a loved one. Patience, understanding and kindness can make a huge difference to so many and costs nothing."
Jane Moore, joint founder of the Purple Angel Dementia Campaign and fellow carer

"Having known Tony and Barbara for over 5 years, I found it very moving and emotional to read their story. I only knew Barbara after she lost her ability to speak but she could tell you how she was feeling with her eyes, and she always reached out a hand to hold yours. Her love for Tony (and his for her) was apparent in every moment I spent with them. Tony was her rock; she sought him out wherever she was and beamed the biggest smile when she saw him. This inspirational couple have done so much to raise awareness of dementia in Bristol and beyond – Tony by sharing his passion and drive and Barbara by showing the very human side of the disease. Together, they have enabled thousands of people to learn about dementia. This book is the chance to learn more about their story."
Sam Rock Cooper, BDAA employee

"I found the book really informative and can resonate with the frustration in getting support, especially from the point of view of access to support systems for the carer, as well as the person you are caring for."
Angela, a carer

Acknowledgements

I would like to take this opportunity to thank all those people mentioned in this book that have travelled our journey with dementia: my family, friends and the myriad of lovely kind people we have met over the years, particularly in the last twenty or so.
Tony Hall

Preface

"What d'you want for Christmas Dad?" my eldest daughter asked.

I thought for a moment and then replied, "A bucketful of patience my love."

She gave me a wry smile, knowing what that meant.

You see, her mum and my wife, Barbara, had Early Onset Dementia, later diagnosed as Frontal Temporal Dementia (FTD). Barbara was only fifty-three years old when she started to show symptoms.

Living with someone who has dementia demands patience, not just on the person caring, but on the part of the whole family and friends. People lose patience - particularly wives, husbands, mothers, fathers, and other close relatives, because they don't understand what dementia is, or what's going on; they take things personally rather than see it in the context of the person having a terminal condition.

Dementia is caused by diseases of the brain which can affect personality, behaviour, memory, rationality and create confusion. It makes the individual unrecognisable from the one you've known for years. Sweet, little old ladies, who have never been sharp or sworn in their lives, suddenly begin to use language which would pay credit to a Regimental Sergeant Major in the military. Of course, the opposite can also happen, people who were loud or outgoing can suddenly become as quiet as a mouse. It is an insidious condition.

Dementia can be compared to child development in reverse. If you think about how we develop as people, we start off as babies, then toddlers, children, teenagers, adults, middle-aged, then seniors. At each stage, we gather more information and skills.

With dementia however, the reverse is happening. They may lose some of that information, or some of those skills that they've accumulated over their lives, until they become unrecognisable from the person you've known for years.

This is the heartache of living with someone who has dementia.

The most common type of dementia is Alzheimer's Disease; 70 – 80% of people with dementia have Alzheimer's Disease. Other common ones are Vascular Dementia, Frontal Temporal Dementia (FTD), sometimes called Picks Disease and Dementia with Lewy Bodies. But there are around two hundred different types of dementia according to the Alzheimer's Society.

There are currently 950,000 people living with dementia in the country, expected to increase to one million by 2025. Approximately 5000 of those live in Bristol. At the time of writing, there are approximately 71,000 people nationally with Young Onset Dementia (i.e. they are of working age). Approximately 1000 of those people live in Bristol, some are still working, some are not.

A common myth is that when you grow older, you will contract dementia. This is not correct. According to the Alzheimer's Society, one in fourteen people over 65 will develop it and one in three over 80. It is not a natural part of the ageing process.

Why has this book been written? I've never written a book before.

As Barbara and I have travelled along the dementia journey over the last twenty years, I have been asked several times to write a book about our experiences.

This is it.

My dream is that it will resonate with fellow travellers and be useful, as well as interesting. It will never be a literary best seller, but if helps one person in their struggle, it will be worth all the effort.

You see, the journey with dementia is a struggle. This book is about the struggle of an ordinary common or garden family, coping with the fact that their wife, mother and grandmother changed from the person the family had known and been brought up by, to one that became unrecognisable.

It talks of trying to come to terms with the fact that this once ordinary housewife and nursery nurse gradually deteriorated before their very eyes. The woman she was totally changed over two decades because of this awful disease. We are not experts, nor do we have letters after our name, we attended the "School of Hard Knocks" and the "University of Life", but within these pages there are hopefully some useful tips on what to do and what not to do.

It's also a struggle with faith too. Barbara and I are Christians, but I am angry with God. Our daughter Janice was allowed to contract Leukaemia. She died on Good Friday, which is today as I write this, so Good Friday has a double meaning for us as a family, Jesus being crucified and Janice dying. She was six years old when she died. Over the years I have (sort of) come to terms with this and it has given me an understanding of what it's like to lose a child and so brought me to really empathise with parents in a similar situation or going through it.

But now my wife!

Why does God allow a woman, a grandmother who has so much to give, to contract this awful debilitating disease? People close to me know that I believe grandparents are really important in the family structure, in fact they are generally the cement that holds the family together. My grandchildren have lost so much. I try to be Nanny as well as Grandad, and fail miserably, so they have lost both of us.

Christianity gives us hope because it believes in resurrection, so one day we will see Janice and Barbara again, but that doesn't remove the hurt we're feeling right now. Kind and well-meaning people who refer me to Job's story in the Old Testament of the Bible, seem to gloss over or ignore the pain we're suffering at this moment.

(Job was a very rich and righteous man who was tested by God and Satan for his faithfulness. He lives through a series of catastrophes, but remains true to God, who in the end, blesses him even more for his loyalty.)

You will read in this book about Bristol Dementia Action Alliance (BDAA). I launched it in 2013 because it is the only way I can fight this disease. I'm not a doctor or scientist, I can't find a cure. Even if a cure was found today, it wouldn't have helped Barbara. The only way I can fight dementia is by increasing understanding and awareness, trying to build a dementia friendly community. BDAA is in the "education business" because millions of people think dementia is just a memory problem, but it's a lot more than that and can destroy families. If you'd told me ten years ago that I would become the Chair of a dementia charity, I would have laughed you out of court.

I pray that this book helps to achieve my dream.

1962 – 1979: Beginnings

I am Barbara's carer. I hate the word, I am not Barbara's carer, I'm her husband. I care for her, but then I've cared for her since the first time I took her out during the winter of 1962/3, which older readers will recognise as one of the worst on record. We had snow for weeks, even months, with football matches being postponed, some several times.

On our first date, we went to the cinema at Gants Hill, Ilford, near Hainault where Barbara lived. She held onto my arm because the pavement was slippery due to the snow, which relaxed me and we got on like a house on fire, she even laughed at my jokes! I took her home and we shared her umbrella. I took her home because I wanted to make sure she got there safely, I cared, and I've cared for her ever since.

Barbara was sixteen when we met, sweet sixteen, a receptionist/switchboard operator with a New Zealand publishing firm located near St. Paul's Cathedral in London. I was seventeen and an apprentice telephone engineer with Post Office Engineering, later to become British Telecom. I was allocated to a chap called Ron who was installing a new automatic switchboard for her firm. I was a bit grumpy at the time because I'd just been dumped by a previous girlfriend, so Ron suggested that I ask Barbara out, in fact he dared me! At the time, I was one of those people who couldn't resist a dare, so I asked Barbara for a date and to my surprise, she said "Yes". The rest, as they say, is history.

I remember one occasion when I picked her up from her office in St. Pauls. I was waiting outside when I heard the clickity click of her high-heels and she appeared. A big smile (she was known for her smile) and she kissed me and put her arm through mine. She made me feel good. My girl.

As we walked to catch the tube to go to her home, she asked what we could do that evening.

"Fancy going to the pictures?" I asked (for younger readers, "pictures" is what you call the cinema).

"What's on?"

"Oh, I expect there's a film about boy meets girl, boy asks her out, she accepts, they fall in love, have kids and live happily ever after," I replied, "Just like us really."

She rolled her eyes and looked at me with one of those looks, still smiling she said, "You reckon, do you?"

I said, "Of course, you know it makes sense."

She laughed.

Yes, I admit it, I was a cheeky chappie in those days.

Barbara worked voluntarily at Barnardo's in her spare time and was also a Sunday School teacher. She had a love for children and wanted to study for her Nursery Nurse Education Board (NNEB) qualification and become a nursery nurse. Being the eldest daughter in a family of five children, Barbara was expected to go out to work and help with the family income, her dad saying that there was no money in looking after children.

I am an only child, but I also like and enjoy children. Our dream was to set up and run a children's home. This, however, was against state policy at the time, as the thinking was that children would be better cared for by being fostered or adopted in the community; children's homes were being run down and closed. So, when we got married, we decided to foster as well as have our own children. Friends and family have told us that we achieved our ambition; our house was always full of children!

We got married at Manford Way Evangelical Church in Hainault, Essex on 4th September 1965. I was twenty and Barbara was nineteen. We went to Westward Ho! for our honeymoon, and it rained continually! So, after five days, we decided to go home and spend the rest of our holiday decorating our flat.

We went on to have two daughters, eighteen months apart. Soon after, we moved to Andover in Hampshire where we moved into a three bedroomed house.

Our dreams had come true! We had space and a garden!

Joining the local Baptist Church with our little family unit, everything looked grand, and life was good.

Our happiness was short-lived however because when Janice, our eldest daughter, was five, she became ill and was diagnosed with Leukaemia, and a really aggressive type at that. It was a virulent strain of the condition, and she died six months later in Winchester Hospital on Good Friday, aged six. So Good Friday, as mentioned already, has special meaning for us on two counts. We were devastated and went into depression, but our church family surrounded us with their love and were really outstanding in their care and support for all of us. Gradually, we returned to normal, our normal that is!

We were advised to have another baby, not as a replacement, Janice could never be replaced, but as a new addition to our family. Every child is precious and can never be replaced.

We had also applied to become foster parents and were informally "fostering" a girl from our church.

Our vision of running a children's home was now becoming a reality, as all our dreams bore fruit and we went from one child to four in a year, with three extra additions.

Melanie arrived in February 1974, aged two and a half, on a long-term fostering arrangement.

Ruth was born in April 1974.

Steve arrived from Vietnam on 7th April 1975.

Barbara had seen a piece on the TV covering the work of an organisation called Project Vietnam Orphans which helped and supported orphans in that country during the American War. Children were being sponsored by people in the UK and USA, some were even being formally adopted. Initially, we sent sponsorship money to a Catholic order of nuns in Vietnam looking after and caring for the orphaned children, but when we realised some of these children were being adopted in England, we applied to adopt a child too.

It's a long story (and perhaps another book!), but Steve arrived on 7th April 1975 aged six months, amongst a hail of publicity because he had been one of 101 children flown to the UK by the Daily Mail in the well publicised "mercy flight". The American/Vietnam war was coming to a climax and finally ended with Vietnam formally reunified on 1st May 1975.

Once again, our church family were fabulous in their love, care and support for us. They provided a cot for Steve, and we didn't have to buy him any clothes until he was five!

Although different personalities, Barbara and I were a good team and worked well together. She was the "original independent woman"; probably the result of being the eldest daughter, but she was quite reserved in a lot of ways and was most comfortable when working in the background, whereas I'm the one up front.

Over the next few years, life was spent bringing up our family. We also worked with children and young people at church, until in 1979 I was promoted at work, and we moved to Bristol.

We again joined the local Baptist Church and became involved with children and young people. Barbara became a Brownie Guider; I became a youth leader.

For years Barbara had talked about sitting her formal NNEB qualification and become a trained nursery nurse. At the dinner table one day, she announced that she'd seen an NNEB course advertised at our local college. We all looked at each other and then at her and said in unison, "Do it!" She'd been talking about it for years and now was her opportunity. Needless to say, she passed with distinction, as we all knew she would, because she had years of experience with mothers & toddlers' groups, pre-school, children with special needs, Sunday School, Covenanters and youth work. The teacher often used her and her life stories as visual aids.

As a result of her NNEB, our minister asked her to use her experience and get involved in our church mothers and toddlers' group to suggest ways in which we could better meet the needs of families. This she did and the new group was called Chatterbox.

In 1995, I took early voluntary retirement from BT and went to work with Czech Telecom (SPT), mainly based in Prague, as a contractor/consultant with a team of ex-BT guys led by my old boss. This was a great opportunity for me, and I generally worked two weeks on, two weeks off. Sometimes, Barbara came out there with me and on a couple of visits did her NNEB assignments whilst I was at work. The contract ended in 2000 and we came back to the UK permanently.

1999: Dementia Looms

Looking back, it's difficult to determine exactly when Barbara's dementia really started; there were probably signs there when we moved house from Horfield to Westbury-on-Trym in November 1999.

She decided at this time that she would become a registered childminder. It seems amazing now that she could cope with this. She attended the formal training and responded to the Ofsted audits. Our house and garden were totally transformed with more safety gadgets. The paperwork, stress and red tape were horrendous, but Barbara coped with it all. She loved children and that was the motivating driving force.

I'm not an avid diary writer, but a note in my diary in 2002 says "Came home from work today to find Barbara upset and crying."

I asked her, "What's the matter, why are you crying?"

She said, "Oh, I went to get some money out of the "hole in the wall" at the bank this afternoon and couldn't remember my pin number."

We've all done that of course and we haven't got dementia, so it didn't really register until later.

I said to her, "Well, that's OK, if you need some cash, we'll go and get some tomorrow. Don't cry," and I gave her a hug.

Although we had moved house, Barbara still felt committed to Chatterbox, as it was a fairly new venture and becoming more and more popular with local young families. She carried on leading it until 2003 when we decided to move to our local Baptist church in Westbury and become members there. It wasn't long after that Barbara was invited to join their mothers and toddlers' group, called WotsTots.

As well as this, Barbara sometimes looked after our grandsons, whilst I went to work.

So, our house was generally full of children!

In March 2005, on the advice of our GP, Barbara had to resign from childminding. Her general planning and organising had started to suffer and it was all becoming too much for her to cope with. This was a bitter blow to her, but it was around this time that I thought we would have a big party to celebrate our 40th wedding anniversary, retake our wedding vows at church and perhaps go on a cruise. We both love "boats and trains and planes". (Song title there somewhere!). We did do this and sailed around the Norwegian fjords. Stunningly beautiful, and that was just Barbara! This holiday really made up for our disastrous honeymoon at Westward Ho! all those years ago.

As well as the incident involving Barbara forgetting her pin number, another real sign of Barbara's dementia that I can remember was when she said to me "I can't remember the children's birthdays anymore, what mother can't remember her children's birthdays? I brought them into the world."

So, I said to her, "Well if you're worried, let's go and see the doctor."

He referred us to a consultant at Southmead Hospital, who we only actually met eighteen months later. This was a situation my NHS friends that I formed later are really embarrassed about. Back then though, mental health, under which dementia came, was the "Aunt Sally of the NHS", some say it still is! Personally, I don't think dementia is a mental health issue, it is a physical condition (a disease of the brain) with mental health implications and effects.

I hadn't told my children what I suspected about Barbara's memory problems. When I did eventually tell them that I thought she had dementia, they were naturally very upset, even angry, that I had kept it to myself. They had wondered why she had been behaving differently. I told them that, as her husband, I was trying to protect her and making excuses for her. Although this was probably understandable, it was totally wrong of me, I apologised to them and said that they should have been included in what was going on. We would deal with this as a family and support each other.

Our eldest daughter had presented us with grandson back in June 2002, just at the time when a daughter needs her mum for support and advice. I remember having a conversation with her where she said, "Can I really trust Mum's advice now?" I told her to still ask Barbara's opinion, include her in a conversation as normal and then make her own judgement call as to whether it seemed sound or not. Even now, she says she lost her mum at a time when she really needed her. She could still talk to me of course, but there are a lot of things a girl needs her mum for.

On the outside, and to everyone else, it seemed that Barbara was OK, although I felt she made some strange decisions at times. We even did a talk together at church about a visit to Vietnam we had made to the Sisters, a Catholic order of nuns, who had initially cared for Steve when he was abandoned as a baby in Vietnam.

As a family however, we could see a definite change in Barbara's personality and behaviour. As Christians, we believed in the healing power of God, so as a family we began praying for healing. We also had prayer meetings with friends and church groups. She wasn't healed in the sense that her dementia was taken away, but we felt that she had been made "whole". She was in His hands. "Healing" has different meanings to different people.

Eventually, Barbara got her appointment with the consultant.

His first diagnosis was that Barbara had depression. I replied that, in my opinion she didn't have depression, we'd seen depression in the family years ago when our daughter Janice was ill and had subsequently died. We all get a bit fed up at times, but I didn't think she had depression and suggested to him that, from articles I had read on the internet, it looked like she had Early Onset Dementia. I'm not a doctor, but to my surprise he said that he would send her for an MRI scan.

As stated earlier, I'm not an avid diary keeper, but I had started to make a few notes to record the progression of Barbara's condition. An entry for our annual newsletter to family and friends in December 2006 recorded that:

Barbara had a brain scan which disclosed that some cells around the brain's periphery had degenerated. This can happen in old age, but not normally for someone in their late fifties. She also saw a Neuropsychologist who spent three hours giving her various IQ tests. She came out of this feeling positive, as she felt she was not as bad as she thought she was. Following more recent trips to the hospital, the consultant has agreed to give her another scan and more tests next February 2007, a year after the last ones, to see if the problem is getting worse.

On the bright side, although some of her brain cells have degenerated, like all of us, she has others that have never been used. She is, therefore, trying to stimulate some of these cells into action by getting regular exercise by walking, reading, doing Sudoku, keeping a diary and attending a bible study group which needs a lot of reading and preparation. As well as this, she is Creche Coordinator on the committee for WotsTots and she also looks after our grandson on Wednesdays.

Alzheimer's Disease usually starts by affecting people's short-term memory, but this wasn't the case with Barbara. Forgetting our children's birthdays wasn't a short-term issue. A short-term memory problem is forgetting what you had for breakfast this morning or, indeed, did you have breakfast this morning?

Have you ever gone up the stairs at home and, when you got to the top, forgotten what you went up there for? That is not a short-term memory problem, that is a "senior moment" from which we all suffer occasionally! It's a bit like bending down to pick up something from the floor and thinking "What else can I do while I'm down here?" These are "senior moments", not short-term memory problems; short term memory issues are consistent, you know you have a problem and so does everyone else.

When asked what dementia is, most people answer "memory problems". It presents itself in lots of other ways too. Here's a few:

Repetition: People with dementia can repeat themselves by asking the same question over and over again, "What's the time?" or "What's for dinner?" You answer them and they ask the same question ten seconds later. It can become quite wearing, but a way to deal with it is the same as we handle a toddler who keeps repeating themselves. We change the subject to try to switch their brain into thinking about something else. It doesn't always work but is worth a try and much better than getting frustrated or angry.

Planning: You may also notice and become aware that their planning and organising skills are being affected. They may not be able to dress themselves properly, clothes may be put on in the wrong order or not changed regularly, resulting in them becoming smelly.

Spatial awareness: You may have heard the term "Oh, he or she has become a wanderer." This is not a very nice term or way to refer to some who has a condition they have no control over, but it's due to a failing in "spatial awareness", knowing how to find their way around or looking for familiar things.

Money handling: On the weekly shop at the supermarket, you may see a person at the checkout having a problem counting out their money or trying to remember their pin number. Whilst they're doing this, time is going by and, because people are impatient, we can often hear "tutting" or moaning because everybody is in a hurry. I hope you're not one of them! What we can do is offer to help by simply saying "Excuse me, but are you having a problem with your money or card? Can I help?" They may turn round to you and say, "Thank you" or "Yes please" or "No thanks, I'm fine", but in that moment, their brain has been distracted by talking to you and when they switch back, they may remember "Oh pin, that's the four-digit code" and they remember. It doesn't always work, but better than whinging at their slowness!

In the last few years, some supermarkets have recognised this issue and created what they call "Dementia Friendly mornings", by which I mean that they have a certain time on a certain day in the week when they create "slow lanes", where people who need time are given it, whilst everyone else uses the other lanes.

Staring: On walking along the street, the person in front of you suddenly stops and acts like a statue and is seen to stare. This is referred to as a Catatonic Trance. It may take minutes before they come out of it. The thing to do here is to firstly watch to see if they remain still and that they don't put themselves in any danger. When they move and begin to walk again, gently reassure them that everything is OK.

When talking to a person with dementia don't rush. First, obtain and maintain eye contact, talk to them clearly and slowly. You may have to repeat yourself. When their eyes tell you that they've understood, move on to the next thing you want to say. People with dementia can't be rushed, we need to communicate at their speed.

Dementia can also cause people to be confused, their brain taking some time to analyse what is being said to them. Again, we need to establish eye contact, speak slowly and clearly as above.

Colours and patterns: Research has also shown that people with dementia may also have problems with colours and perception. As we were to learn later in our journey, an example of this is black mats. Taking a person with perception problems up to a black mat, you and I will see a black mat, but they might see a hole. If you try to walk across the mat, they will become anxious and hang on to you, as we don't walk across holes, they're dangerous. Even if you walk closely around it, they remain anxious.

They can also have issues with carpets. If they see a carpet with concentric rectangles on it with straight lines in the centre, they may see a fishpond. If it has wiggly lines in the middle, they may see a snake-pit.

(These findings are the result of research at Stirling University in Scotland and are available at length through their website).

2007: Diagnosis

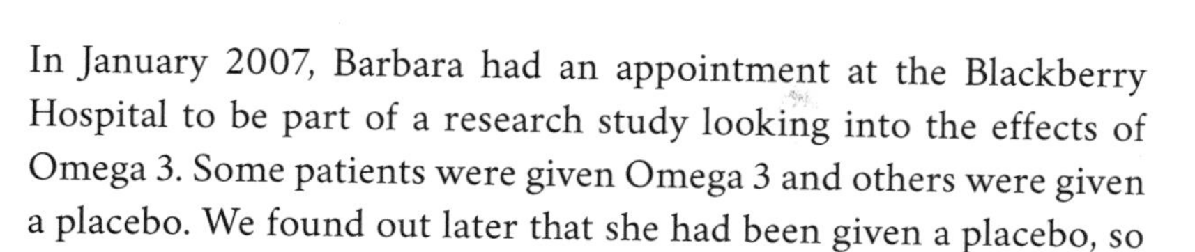

In January 2007, Barbara had an appointment at the Blackberry Hospital to be part of a research study looking into the effects of Omega 3. Some patients were given Omega 3 and others were given a placebo. We found out later that she had been given a placebo, so nothing changed.

During the 2006/07 Christmas holidays, I had suggested to Barbara that if she needed me at home, I would leave work and take early voluntary retirement. A couple of months later she said that she was beginning to like the idea of having me at home (not many wives say that!). So, I left work in July and joined Barbara in the kitchen at WotsTots serving refreshments, where, due to her dementia, she had moved from directly being involved with the mums and children, to handing out the orange juice and biscuits to everyone. The team and the mums were very understanding of Barbara's illness and still included her in their conversations. I also took a turn at reading a story to the children and singing with them (not that I'm a good singer!), but it was fun, and the children enjoyed the action songs.

Also in July, Barbara had an appointment with a second neuropsychologist. This appointment and test proved that her memory had got worse. Despite saying to the contrary in the earlier appointment, we were now informed that she had the early signs of Alzheimer's Disease. There is currently no known cure (genetics may be a long-term answer), but drugs can slow down the degeneration of the brain cells. Physical and mental exercise can also slow it down, and, as you will appreciate, Barbara pursued these with great energy, vigour and enthusiasm, as she doesn't give in easily! We had decided that we would fight this illness with everything we'd got. Appointments with consultants for various physical ailments however, left her extremely frustrated, particularly as she had to retire from working directly with children after forty odd years, just handing out the orange juice and biscuits.

The consultant prescribed her Aricept, which did nothing for her condition as it's an anti-depressant, so at the next consultation, he prescribed Galanteline, which took her taste of food away. It also involves a step up dosage i.e. you take 4mg twice a day for a fortnight, then step it up to 8mg and then 12mg. The first two weeks were fine, but when she changed dosage from 4mg to 8mg on the Friday, the day after, Saturday, she was rolling around on the lounge floor in agony and I thought that she was going to die. I told her that she wasn't going to take any more of this stuff and we returned to the GP to tell him what had happened. He referred us back to the consultant who said that he was sorry that the drugs hadn't had a positive effect, but there was no further treatment available and suggested I contact the Alzheimer's Society. He also referred her to the Memory Clinic which, at the time, had a four-month waiting list for appointments.

At this point I felt abandoned by the NHS!

There was also talk of statins. As I've said before, I'm not a doctor or an expert, but I do have great reservations about the use of statins. Administered properly, they probably have a place, but stories I have heard about their use (or should I say misuse) from fellow carers, have engrained in me a mistrust for the use of these drugs. I feel that often, they are used just to keep people "quiet", they are used to control people.

As well as seeing the consultant, Barbara was also seeing various other medics including a lovely speech therapist named Kathy, who had come to the UK from New Zealand. This was because Barbara was using the wrong words in conversation. For example, she would come in from the garden and say, "I've just picked some apples in the greenhouse", whereas I knew she meant tomatoes. So, because she used the wrong words, Kathy would go through some flashcards with Barbara to see if she could identify the pictures. One case I remember well was a caravan. Barbara could tell you everything about caravans, we go on holiday in that, we see a lot of those on the road etc, everything except that it was called a caravan.

During one such session, Kathy queried the diagnosis of

Alzheimer's Disease and said "She has dementia, no doubt about that, but I think she has Semantic or Frontal Temporal Dementia (FTD) because some of her memory problems are word- related.

"As it happens, an Australian friend of mine, who came to the UK when I came over from New Zealand, is conducting research into FTD at University College Hospital (UCL) in London. Do you think Barbara would be interested in being part of the research?"

So, I said, "Well ask her."

Barbara was able to make decisions like that for herself at the time and like lots of people, she would do anything that brought about a greater good to people. We went to UCL in November.

We had to be there early for our appointment, so we stayed overnight with some friends of ours in Harrow, Bernice and Frank, and got the tube into central London to arrive on time. Researchers conducted various tests over the next two days, including scans and psychological tests, then we were called into the office for the diagnosis.

The researcher said "From the procedures we've carried out, we are pretty sure that Barbara does have Frontal Temporal Dementia and, yes, there is no treatment. We suggest that you contact the Alzheimer's Society."

Once again, I felt abandoned by the NHS!

I was shocked and amazed. If we have a medical problem, we automatically go to the doctor. We are either given medicine or treatment to make it better, or are referred to other medics at a hospital to carry out some sort of operation. This didn't happen.

I am not blaming the NHS. The issue at the time was that there was not a great deal known about dementia. What was needed then, and is still the same today, is research, which in turn requires money!

Funding for dementia was sadly lacking, although in 2021 when this book is being written, the situation is improving due to high profile celebrities like Terry Pratchett, Prunella Scales and Barbara Windsor recently contracting dementia. Awareness of the condition is all over the media. Alan Shearer had a programme on TV suggesting that heading a football contributes to players contracting dementia; people are becoming more aware. Chris Sutton has recently written an article stating that dementia may have killed his dad prematurely. Funding from the public is increasing, albeit slowly, but more is needed to find a cure and there is still a long way to go. Stigma, denial and embarrassment of dementia still exists, despite brilliant work in setting up dementia friendly communities. The profile of dementia is where cancer was thirty years ago. We used to whisper, "They've got the "BIG C", but we now talk quite openly about cancer. Nowadays we whisper, "They've got the "BIG D."

As one carer put it:

"Mention cancer and everyone comes running, mention dementia and everyone disappears."

I'm not saying that cancer shouldn't receive funding. I'm saying that dementia needs research funding too and this needs to be addressed.

***

What could I do to make Barbara better?

Unfortunately, I couldn't find a cure, I'm not a research scientist.

Dementia is a progressive, terminal disease, but I could keep her active and slow it down.

When we got home, we obviously talked about the diagnosis. Barbara said, "I'm going to get worse, aren't I?"

I replied, "Yes, I'm afraid you are, but I will look after you though, you're my wife."

You see, when we made our marriage vows, we meant them. When we said, "In sickness and in health", we meant it. We'd had many years of good health, now we faced a period of not so good. I knew if the situation was reversed and it was me that was ill, Barbara would do everything she could to look after me, she had done so for forty-odd years.

Barbara said to me "I want you to get married again, you can't live on your own, find a nice girl and get married again."

("Girl" I thought, we're in our fifties!)

I replied, "I don't want anyone else; I love you and want you, I will look after you."

She was still caring for me even though she was seriously ill.

So, there was no medical treatment, what were we to do?

There's a common saying that goes "what's good for the heart is good for the brain", so daily exercise and a balanced diet were even more essential now than they had ever been before. We were walkers anyway, so exercise wasn't a problem, we walked everywhere. Barbara had always been an advocate of a good balanced diet, so that wasn't a problem either and so I continued in similar vein.

We certainly weren't going to give in to the dementia, we would fight it all the way. We kept her brain stimulated with physical exercise, intellectual exercise and social exercise.

Barbara enjoyed Sudoku and jigsaw puzzles. She always had a jigsaw puzzle on the go on our living room table. She was still reading her Bible in the conservatory every morning and praying for our children. This added to her intellectual and social exercise.

On Boxing Day 2007, whilst doing a jigsaw puzzle with Barbara, I spent some time thinking about her illness and what additional support we needed. Family and friends were very concerned and had all asked what they could do to help Barbara (and me). To stimulate her brain, we needed to keep talking to Barbara and give her tasks to do, for example helping with cooking meals.

Barbara was a good cook and had taught all our children to cook (I wish she had taught me, I had to learn the hard way from scratch!). We would treat her as normally as possible and perhaps folk could send her regular emails or phone her. Her cousin Maureen was one who did this.

We are a close family and if there was a problem, we would hold what we call "a family conference". We held such a meeting because of the diagnosis. Dementia doesn't just affect the individual, it affects the whole family, friends and social groups.

After discussing Barbara's condition for some time, my eldest daughter said, "D'you know Dad, Mum's not the problem here, you are." Quite blunt I thought!

"What!" I replied, "I'm not ill."

She said, "Think about it, Mum's got dementia, she didn't ask to have dementia, there's nothing she can do about her dementia, there's little or no treatment and no cure, the only thing that can change is you, and us as a family and us as a community. We must learn to deal with it."

After thinking about what she said for those few moments, I concluded that she was absolutely right, the only people that can change is us. That is the driving force behind the Bristol Dementia Action Alliance (which we'll come onto later).

Our youngest daughter, Ruth, offered to move back from Cornwall to help me look after Barbara. By this time, she and her husband had two young boys. I said to her "That's very kind and considerate of you, but stay where you are and bring up your family. If I need you, I know where you are."

Some of our friends had come across a group for people with dementia. It was held at another local church, Tyndale Baptist Church, on Thursdays. Carers could leave their loved ones there to be cared for by two lovely ladies called Maureen and Margaret, supported by a group of volunteers.

This was music to my ears! It meant a few hours of respite. Carers generally don't mind caring, they just need some time off to be themselves occasionally.

And so, Barbara attended the group.

2008: Support

In March we were visited by Sally from the Alzheimer's Society, who became our Dementia Support Worker (DSW).

Sally invited us to a drop-in centre which she supported at Westbury Methodist Church Hall. It met every Tuesday fortnight for two hours and was open to carers and people with dementia. Like a lot of people, our initial instinct was that we didn't really want to go along to a group with geriatrics (not very kind of us, but we still considered ourselves to be young, but we'd give it a try). To our surprise, two other couples around our age had also started to attend within six weeks of each other.

We got talking and discovered we all liked walking and so we set up a walking group, on the alternate Tuesdays to the drop in. We arranged about a dozen walks within a ten-to-fifteen-mile radius of where we lived. We would meet at an agreed starting point, go for a walk for an hour or two, depending on the capability of those walking, and then finish at a tea-room, coffee shop or pub for a drink or lunch. Normal activity.

At the day centre, we had the statutory tea and biscuits (and occasional cake, the country runs on cake as we all know!) and an arranged activity like a quiz, craft activities, art or sometimes a visiting group. One week Sally brought along a light, plastic beach-ball and I organised a game of football for the men. They loved it! Making birthday cards or colouring is seen by some guys as "kids' stuff", a lot of men like to do something physical.

So, we were now doing the three things that we could do to fight her dementia in the absence of treatment or drugs: intellectual exercise, physical exercise and social exercise. We didn't take tablets anyway if we got a headache, we'd go for a walk.

Sally also set up a monthly Carers Support Group, where, if carers could leave the person they were looking after for an hour or two, they could attend the group. The group comprised mainly of women, and we discussed the various issues we faced as carers. There was obviously a lot of common ground - frustration, stress, tiredness, ability to cope, no time to be ourselves, statutory allowances and benefits, to name but a few.

Our discussions were all confidential and what was said in the room stayed in the room. People found that under these circumstances they could open up and share quite honestly. We empathised, laughed, cried and sometimes even screamed together and found that we all understood. We also learnt a lot. As one carer put it:

"You don't volunteer to become a carer do you, it creeps up on you."

"When you become a carer, you don't know what you don't know."

So, in this regard, the group was very helpful.

For example, I didn't know you could get a discount on your council tax if you were in our position. Also, benefits for cancer care are budgeted for by the NHS, but dementia is not. Why is that? Both are conditions we have no control over.

It was surprising how many issues were common to all of us:

1. They felt trapped and on their own.
2. They felt exhausted.
3. Nearest family were two hundred miles away (That's if they had any family at all that were interested in helping).
4. Care may be reliant on one sibling.
5. There was a general lack of support.
6. Trying to keep people with dementia active and their brain stimulated was difficult, as they weren't always interested in doing anything suggested.

The value of regular Carers Support Groups can be recognised as these issues (and others) need raising; discussion and coping mechanisms enable the carer to avoid becoming ill themselves.

A common message we shared was:

"You're not on your own."

Flavour of the month at the time, and which I am totally in favour of, was:

"Care for the Carer."

This initiative put a lot of emphasis on caring for the carer because if the carer fell ill, the responsibility of looking after the person with dementia would fall on other members of the family, friends or the state.

Another strapline we encountered at this time was:

"Person Centred Care."

Instead of everyone being treated the same, particularly in care homes and day centres, individuals have different needs and therefore would need their varying needs to be met. (I also approve very strongly of this too!).

There was an occasion I remember when Barbara was driving our car. This was unusual, because when we travelled together in the car, it would generally be me driving. On this occasion though, she was driving. On a local road near our home, she drove down the hill, around a long-left-hand curve narrowly missing two parked cars by a gnat's kneecap.

This got me worried, particularly as on another occasion, she was in the right-hand lane at traffic lights. When the lights turned green, she went forward, straight in front of an articulated lorry.

As a result of these two incidents, I questioned whether she should still be driving at all. I said to her, "If that had been two children and you had hit them causing serious harm or, even worse, you killed them, you'd never forgive yourself; maybe it's time for you to stop driving."

I also mentioned this at the carers group and learnt that you must inform the DVLA when a person has dementia, because the condition can affect the ability to concentrate and drive properly. Failure to notify them could result in a fine of up to £1000.

Incidentally, when informing the DVLA, there are several actions that can be taken:

- A GP / Optometrist can examine you and pass you as having

good eyesight.

- You can be placed under an annual review.
- You can have your licence taken away.

Barbara stopped driving and never renewed her licence.

Although Barbara was still doing the cooking, one day she put a pizza in the oven with the cardboard plate still in situ. Fortunately, I discovered this in time and rescued the situation, thus preventing a fire.

Again, I raised this issue at the carers group, and someone said, "I've done that, and I haven't got dementia. See if it happens again and, if so, step in then and don't let her cook." So, from then on, I supervised her cooking.

We don't have pizzas that often, but a couple of months later, it happened again, or would have done if I hadn't intervened. From then on, I gradually took over cooking.

I realised that there are lots of potential dangers in the kitchen for people with dementia, which I've listed separately later in the book.

When you become a carer, or realise you are one, you must also adopt the role of the person you live with as well as your own.

As husband and wife, and like other married couples, we had agreed on "who does what" in the house. Barbara took on the typical woman's jobs and I took on the typical man's jobs. For many couples I know, if the wife falls ill to dementia, the husband must do the cleaning, cooking etc, either by doing it himself, or by getting it done by someone else or professionally. Similarly with the wife, she may have to get the car serviced, get a professional to do the DIY or dig the garden herself for example.

When I realised Barbara could no longer be Nanny as she would like to be, I tried to be Mum as well as Dad, Nanny as well as Grandad. People that know me will tell you that I place great importance on grandparents, particularly the grandmother, because they have so much to give their grandchildren. One of my saddest regrets is realising that Barbara had so much to give ours and it was taken away by this awful disease. It also affected my relationship with our grandchildren too. As well as giving them unconditional love, I could no longer do things with them that I wanted to, because my first priority was to Barbara and her care.

***

The strange thing about dementia is the speed at which it progresses. People would say to me, "How long do you think she's got?" Not very nice to hear, but people do ask! Sometimes they would ask, "How long does this go on for?" There's no single answer to this question, but there's a common saying:

"If you've met one person with dementia,
you've met one person with dementia."

They are all different, just the same as we as people are all different. We have similarities, but each one of us is unique. There is no one in the world like you and no one like me.

As an example of this, let me tell you about a fellow carer whose husband had FTD, the same as Barbara. He died within six months. Barbara had symptoms for around twenty years. We are all different and have different ways of dealing with things. They supposedly had the same condition, but with differing outcomes over differing time spans. People with dementia are all different.

People also often remark "You don't look as though you've got dementia." Because on the outside, people may look perfectly "normal".

We don't have "I've got dementia" tattooed on our foreheads, do we?

Our response to this is "What does a person with dementia look like then?"

It's only when they open their mouths to speak or behave unusually, that they signal something is different or amiss.

People with dementia are often referred to as "dementia sufferers". These folk already feel that they are a burden to their loved ones and friends, so to refer to them as "sufferers" just makes them feel worse. By calling them "people living with dementia", we are telling the truth without adding to their burden, stigma, embarrassment and isolation.

Someone once asked me "What do you want most?"

I replied that "I want my wife back."

Like most couples, we would sometimes disagree and argue with each other, but on the important major issues, we would agree. You see Barbara wasn't just my wife, she was my best friend and soulmate. One of the things I missed most was not being able to discuss things in the evening. We might discuss the programme we were watching on TV, or what was in the news, and generally put the world to rights. Gradually, we couldn't do that any longer, conversation became more and more difficult. As a result, there was a huge chasm left by her having this illness.

When a person dies you can grieve and feel bereaved. A dictionary definition of grief is "deep sorrow or poignant distress". When a person has dementia, in a sense you lose them twice. You grieve twice, once when the condition arises and secondly when the person finally passes away, then you feel bereaved.

A dictionary definition of bereavement is "deprive of – especially by death".

It is said that there are seven stages of grief:

1. Shock (disbelief) and denial (numbness)
2. Pain and guilt
3. Anger
4. Depression
5. The upward turn
6. Reconstruction and working through
7. Acceptance and hope

A carer for someone living with dementia certainly goes through stages 1 to 4, but there are lots of carers still in stage 4. This is where carers support groups really do play an important and positive part in achieving stages 5 - 7.

Here is an anonymous quote which illustrates the repeated grief:

"So many carers over the past few years have said that when their loved one developed dementia, it was like coping with a living bereavement. They had the person they loved, living with them, but also living so far away from them. As the dementia progressed, they watched helplessly as they saw the distress of their loved ones, not recognising or knowing who they were, or where they lived. It's such a cruel and debilitating disease. It takes a life, then it takes a life all over again."

Guilt is also certainly part of caring too. Almost every carer I've met feels guilty because they don't feel that they're doing enough, even though they may be worn out and exhausted by what they are doing.

At this stage, it's very easy for a person with dementia to feel that their life is over. Similarly for the carer, they may have the same feeling, but it doesn't have to be like this, you can still live reasonably well with dementia.

Let me tell you about a friend of mine. He is married and likes DIY and carpentry. He came home from work one day and said to his wife, "I'm going to have to pack the job in, I can't get my measurements right."

She replied, "What are you going to do then?"

He responded, "I'm going to go to Linkage (a Bristol charity working with the over fifties) and join their cooking class."

So, they went to Linkage and she said to the organiser, "My husband would like to join your cooking class."

"That's OK, Tuesday afternoon at 2.pm."

She said, "But he's got dementia."

The man replied, "That's OK, Tuesday afternoon at 2pm."

She repeated, "Didn't you hear me, he's got dementia!"

The organiser said, "That's OK, if he's got dementia and wants to cook, we'll support him in his cooking."

So, he attends the cooking class and apparently is turning out some very tasty dishes, some are even edible!

I've also heard a story of a lady who was 89 and had dementia. She wanted to do archery!

I hope I'm that positive if I ever reach eighty-nine years of age.

Now both these two people have got a positive outlook. They may have dementia, and they may not be living as well as they used to, but they are living as well as they can, even with the dementia. There is life after diagnosis!

***

In August 2008, I walked Hadrian's Wall with three mates to raise money for the Alzheimer's Society, whilst our children looked after their mum. Travelling from East to West, we stopped at the museum near the Roman fort of Vindolanda. After a short stop for an hour or so, we continued the walk. However, while we had been in the museum, it had poured with rain and as we continued walking, we had to walk on wet grass down a gradient. You can guess what happened! I slipped on the wet grass, put my hand out to stop myself falling and broke my right wrist. We managed to get to a nearby farm, where we called for the emergency services (mobile phones weren't as widespread in those days as they are now!) and I spent the next two nights in Carlisle Infirmary.

Quite ironic really, as I had broken the left wrist the previous year playing football with the children at the Church weekend away in Torquay! Prior to this, I had never broken a limb.

We returned to Hadrian's Wall in September 2009 to finish it off - the walk that is, not the wrist!

In October we returned to UCL as Barbara was still heavily involved in the research project and participating in various tests, mainly psychological.

On recommendation from Sally, we heard about another group at St Monica's Retirement Village called Singing for the Brain. In November we decided to give it a try. Singing is great for fighting dementia as it is:

1. an intellectual exercise - you have to remember the words,
2. a physical exercise - you have to breathe in the right places,
3. a social exercise - you can meet and sing with other people.

I could write another book about the power of singing, but suffice to say that if you sing, keep doing it, it stimulates the brain!

Some common dangers for people living with dementia

Some people with dementia who are for example, in their eighties, may have their brain living in the fifties. Being British, we all like a cup of tea, so if we visited say an eighty-year-old lady and she suggested making a cup of tea, what are the dangers?

1. The first issue may be, can she remember where to make tea? We normally make tea in the kitchen, but can she remember where it is and find her way there?
2. Is her kitchen a modern kitchen or a 1950s kitchen? Chances are, it is not a kitchen straight out of the showroom, neither is it a 1950s kitchen, there's probably been some modernisation and improvements made over the years.
3. Once in the kitchen, one of the things she needs to do is boil water.
   How will she do that?
4. These days, we would generally use an electric kettle, but back in the 1950s, she would probably have used a kettle on a gas hob
   So what are some of the dangers?
5. There's nothing wrong with the kettle, it is produced to a high standard before being sold, the problem is with the user.
6. She could put the electric kettle on the gas hob – not a good idea!
7. The kettle is run on electricity and filled with water.

Electricity and water don't mix!

8. She could forget to switch the kettle on – cold tea!
9. She could switch the kettle on and the water boils – danger of scalding.
10. At each stage of the process, there may be dangers which we need to be aware of and anticipate.

As a result of these dangers, some people wrap their loved one up in cotton wool and do everything for them. This is not advisable, as the result is that you will de-skill the person with dementia before their time. It is much better to let them do things as they are able, but our part is to supervise what they are doing. As the dementia progresses, then we may have to start offering more help and eventually take over.

People with dementia can also be helped to remember where their things are by simple labelling which can be obtained in local shops or over the internet e.g.

1. A picture of a milk bottle/carton with "I live here" written alongside can be placed on the front of the fridge where the milk is kept.
2. A label with a picture of a coffee jar could be placed where the coffee is kept.
3. Similarly, a label with "I live here" and a picture of a loaf of bread could be placed on the front of the bread bin.

Labelling with words and a picture are useful, because some people with dementia may have problems with reading the words but be fine with pictures.

Mechanical aids can also be obtained from local sources or the internet to help the person with dementia cope better with eating and drinking.

Colours can also affect people living with dementia, so particular care needs to be taken when choosing colours for:

- Carpets (plain colours, not busy patterns)
- Curtains (as for carpets)
- Toilets
- Doors
- Corridors
- Walls
- Drinking and eating vessels

I have also read that there is a lot of evidence that colour is important in relation to eating.

A friend of mine who runs a memory café uses plain yellow plates and drinking cups/mugs.

I also came across a US study that had seen a 25% increase in food consumption with red crockery, over any other colour.

I read another story about a chap who got red dinner plates, side plates, bowls and mugs. He gave his sister a red dinner plate and she ate:

- On Sunday, a whole 9" diameter roasted vegetable flan.
- On Monday evening, a whole 9" diameter red pepper and goats' cheese quiche.
- On Tuesday evening, a broccoli and tomato quiche
- On Wednesday, she has had a 'red bowl' of vegetable soup.
- Normally, if he gave her cake she would eat about a quarter and the rest gets crumbled up onto the floor. Today from a 'red side plate' she ate the cake and not a crumb is in sight.

Coincidence? We'll see... but, she has not eaten as well as this for months and the only thing that has changed is the crockery.

2009: Life after Diagnosis

Life was still fairly normal at this stage. We were going out for a walk every day. Sometimes, we walked the three miles to the city centre and walked back again. If Barbara was tired, we used our bus pass for the return journey.

Whilst on a walk with Barbara one day, we saw a camper van with "Adventure before Dementia" written on the side. I said to Barbara, "This is going to be our motto."

We also started spending time with the Drop-In walking group, visiting places like Clifton Downs, Blaise Castle, Coombe Dingle, Snuff Mills, Oldbury Court, Kings Weston Down, Riverside by the Avon, Ashton Court, Bristol Harbourside and Clevedon. After the walk, we would then have a coffee or lunch in a local pub, tea-room, or coffee house.

We were also still visiting friends and they were visiting us. My long-term friends from schooldays, Carol and Russell, dropped in on one occasion and Carol spoke to Barbara directly for quite some time. This really did help to maintain her self-esteem. During that conversation, she asked Barbara a question and I answered. Carol said that she was asking Barbara, I must try not to answer for her. I felt suitably chastised, as this is very common to carers, we very often speak for the person rather than let them answer for themselves.

We were also going out to the theatre occasionally too with our newfound friends at the walking group. Seeing "Joseph" at the Hippodrome with Hilary and Bob was one such occasion.

As a volunteer, I was also working in the shop at Avon Valley Railway once a month. Later in the year, I also became a Santa on the Santa Specials. (The "real Santa" according to a little four-year-old girl I met on the train!). Being Santa was great. I enjoyed it more than the children, as I've never really grown up. There was also the added bonus that the children wanted to have their photo taken with you, so did the mums AND the grandmothers! Great fun!

2009 was also a busy year for visiting various hospitals.

Barbara was having pains in her left leg, and she attended the BRI and Pain Clinic at Frenchay. It turned out eventually to be diagnosed as arthritis.

She was also still attending Southmead to see the speech therapist, UCL for her dementia and St. Michael's Hospital for an ovarian scan – no problems there thank goodness.

Later that year, she also had an Ultrasound at Southmead.

Sally, our Dementia Support Worker, also organised trips out with the Drop-In group. One such trip was to The Beaufort Arms, a pub in Hawkesbury Upton, to play skittles. It wasn't proper skittles; it was a game called "Killer" which kept everybody involved and interested. We had a buffet lunch, a chance to have a drink, be sociable and generally be "normal". This outing was very popular and became an annual event.

Other outings were to Noah's Ark Zoo Farm, Westonbirt Arboretum (the colours of the trees were fantastic) and a trip to Avon Valley Railway which included a boat trip on the river, as well as the train ride. Staff at the railway couldn't have been more friendly and helpful. Between them and the boat owners, they even managed to get wheelchairs for our folks on board, we were all treated like royalty.

Sally also told us about a day centre called The Limes in Kingswood run by the Alzheimer's Society, where her sister worked. It catered for young people with dementia, "young" being defined as under 70. After a couple of telephone calls, Barbara and I were invited with a group of others to an evening supper where we could visit and meet staff.

As a steam railway enthusiast, I was "chuffed" when some friends, Les and Pat, invited us to go with them on a great railway journey across the USA from New York to San Francisco. This would take three weeks and involve legs on seventeen different railways, some of them steam! Other legs were by coach. Barbara really enjoyed railway journeys as well as me, so this trip was right up our street.

It was a great experience, but Barbara was difficult on occasions however, because she kept rounding people up telling them to get back on the coach as it was time to move on. These were thirty-minute stops and we'd only got off the coach ten minutes ago! Again, our fellow travellers were very kind and understanding once they were told that Barbara had dementia.

We have never been to the USA before, so this trip really was the trip of a lifetime. Stops included New York, Washington, Chicago, Denver, Colorado, the Queen Mary, Las Vegas, Hollywood and San Francisco. We also flew across the Grand Canyon on Barbara's birthday as a special treat. Amazing!

Later that year, we had a family holiday in Tavistock, where we rented a large property for the whole family. Barbara enjoyed this very much, as she was with her children and grandchildren.

I am a community person and decided later that year that children in our local primary school took their life in their hands as they crossed the main road to go to school. I applied to be a lolly-pop man. I passed the interview but failed the eye-sight test (but that's another story in itself!), so I asked the head teacher if she needed anyone to listen to the children read. She didn't need asking twice and I went to school on Tuesday afternoons for a couple of hours to listen to them. At this time Barbara could be left at home for short periods, sometimes she would do her jigsaw puzzles.

2010: The Limes

Early in 2010, as Sally had suggested, Barbara started to attend The Limes Day Centre one day per week. On taking her there, I felt like you do on taking your child to school on the first day. I felt very guilty that I was sending my wife to a place to be cared for, when I was her husband, it was my responsibility. I dropped her off at 9am and at 11am I rang Jo, the manager, to see how she was. Of course, she was fine and involved in all the activity. I picked her up at 4pm and the staff said that she'd had a great day involving herself in craft and jigsaw puzzles. When I said that she liked cooking, they even agreed to let her help with the cooking on occasions and she got involved in preparing meals for everyone with the staff (under supervision of course!).

She'd been going there for a couple of weeks, when on one occasion I went to collect her at the end of the day and asked one of the staff, Claire, if I could use their toilet. When I entered the toilet, I noticed that everything was red and white. The door was red, the grab-rail was red, the toilet-seat was red. Everything was red and white.

When I went back into the main lounge, I said to Claire, "Hey Claire, who's the "City" supporter then, your toilet is all red and white!"

"No, it's nothing to do with football," she said, "It's a "Dementia Friendly Toilet". By having a bold colour contrasting with a bland colour, it helps people to identify the facilities better. In the case of the red toilet seat on a bland coloured basin, it prevents 'accidents', particularly from men!

(If you type "Dementia Friendly Toilets" into your internet browser, there are lots of websites spelling out what it is and listing all the tips).

So, there you are, every day is a school day!

I've since found out that students at Stirling University in

Scotland have been conducting lots of research into making buildings and facilities dementia friendly, even how to make your home dementia friendly, toilets being just one area addressed.

Whenever I took Barbara to The Limes, which was ten miles away from home on the other side of the city, Barbara would always insist we travelled the same route. If I deviated from that route to dodge the traffic, she would ask why we were going a different way. She didn't cope well with a change in routine.

When we got there, she would say to me, "You will be OK going home won't you, you won't get lost or involved in any accidents, you have got enough petrol to come and collect me haven't you? You will be back to pick me up at 4 o'clock won't you? Don't cross any roads without looking." This was all anxiety and insecurity based. She was still caring about me as well as herself.

When I went to pick her up one day, a lady called Marie had run the Zumba activity that afternoon. Apparently, according to the staff, Barbara was the first one up!

We were grandparents, as well as parents, and we loved having our grandchildren to stay with us. After all, a grandparent's job is to spoil their grandchildren, isn't it? We then send them home to their parents to play them up. It's called pay-back time!

One Friday night, two of our young grandchildren, aged five and seven, came for a sleepover with Nanny and Grandad.

There we were playing with their toys, well I was playing with their toys, when the younger one said "Grandad, why has Nanny got dementia?"

It's the sort of question a five-year-old will ask and does ask.

So, I had to think for a minute. We've always been honest with our children and grandchildren. We live in the real world, not fantasy land.

I said, "I don't know why Nanny's got dementia, even the doctors and nurses don't really know why we get dementia, they're still trying to find the cause and when they find the cause, they can find a cure. But what's going to happen is when you come over and Nanny makes all those goodies with you, shortbread biscuits, fairy cakes and butterfly cakes, she will not be able to do it anymore. That's because her brain can't remember the ingredients, or she will not be able to read and understand the recipe book.

"She may forget your birthday, but don't worry, I know where Nanny's book is with all your birthdays in, so I'll get the card and the present, so you won't miss out.

"She might even forget your name. It's not that she doesn't like you anymore, it's just that her brain can't remember names. She may even forget my name and I've been married to her for all these years."

So, in this way, I tried to tell him that Nanny's dementia was going to get worse. Dementia is progressive and as a family we faced it together because it affects all of us. And, as a family, we supported each other.

It can be very upsetting when someone with dementia stops recognising you – for you and for them. Some things you can do to help in this situation are:

- put photos of family and friends around their room.
- write their name underneath.
- look at them together.
- wear an item of clothing that they associate with you.
- play music together that they are familiar with.
- do a jigsaw puzzle together.
- discuss happy memories you shared together.

One morning at home, Barbara said that she wanted to go for a walk to The Downs for an hour. I was doing a few jobs around the house, so I said "OK, see you later" and she went for a walk on her own. After about an hour and a half, she hadn't returned, which was strange, so I jumped into the car and drove around The Downs following a route that I knew she normally took. I couldn't find her, so I returned home hoping she was there and that I'd missed her en route.

She wasn't there, so I did a wider search.

To cut a long story very short, she was missing for five hours, and I was beginning to panic.

I was on the way to our local police station to report her as a missing person when I saw her in a side street. I stopped and reassured her that everything was OK.

I said "What are doing all the way up here? I thought you were going to The Downs." She said something along the lines of "Oh, I'm really tired." She was worn out and had also wet herself because she'd been out so long.

I took her home, changed her clothes and gave her some lunch. She never walked by herself since, she would either walk with me, our family, or friends. In fact, a few friends at church kindly formed a rota to take her for a walk while I was helping children with their reading at school.

On telling some support group friends about this incident, one asked if we had a GPS tracker. She said that there were devices on the market whereby a person with dementia could wear one around their neck, on their wrist or in their pocket or bag and a carer could keep track of where they were.

Upon investigation, I discovered that these devices are quite controversial. Some people argued that these devices infringed an individual's personal liberty, whereas others argued that it allowed the person with dementia the freedom to go for a walk independently, with the carer having peace of mind to determine where he/she was at any time if they needed to. As a carer, I'm personally in favour of them.

(BDAA works with Avon & Somerset Police and Avon Fire and Rescue to provide wristbands and hang tags under their Safeguarding Scheme. More information on our website www.bdaa.org.uk)

2011: Person Centred Care

In January, I attended a course on dementia run by a group called SPECAL in Oxfordshire. It was led by a lady whose mother had died with dementia and she taught us the various lessons she had learnt on their journey.

The main thrust of the course was to plan ahead.

Even though the thought of putting your loved one in a care home horrified most of us, we were encouraged to think about it and draw up an "End of Life Plan" (EOL Plan).

I had the stereotypical view of care homes, and my plan was that I'll be on my knees before I put Barbara in a care home! I would care for her at home and keep her as active as possible. A care home was the last resort.

Dementia is scary and affects a person in various stages, it's progressive, but it's useful to know what lies ahead, plan for it and react to it. It is a process of continuous adjustment.

Changes in personality and behaviours may be difficult to cope with, but don't take behaviour personally and blame the loved one, it's the dementia talking.

Naturally the EOL Plan included looking at care homes. In my experience, and in talking to fellow carers and visiting some care homes over the last twenty years, there are good care homes, average care homes and some that ought to be called "don't care homes". (I write later in this book about our personal experience of one such care home). I don't blame the staff for the care, or lack of it, some don't receive the appropriate training or support. I blame the owner or manager, they set the values, standards, tone and culture.

If you look for a care home and upon entering the building you smell urine, walk straight out again. To me this says residents are not being looked after properly. I visited a care home where this was the case, it smelt of urine on entering the building. It closed two months later.

If you ask if they've got an "Activities Coordinator" and they say, "Oh yes", ask what activities they co-ordinate. If the reply is "We have a disco on Tuesday nights" and nothing else is on offer, walk straight out because they are not providing person centred care; different people have different needs. There is nothing wrong with discos incidentally because there is tremendous power in music and song, particularly for people with dementia because it stimulates their brain and memory. However, an activities co-ordinator should be arranging all sorts of activities like craft, table games, board games, gardening and games where you have fun and socialise, as well as being active.

One home I visited was brilliant, it created a "street" in the garden with a pub, post office, grocery store and a couple of other shops. It also had a bus stop. Residents, particularly those with dementia, can walk down "Memory Lane", socialise and reminisce. Really helpful, as this is behaving "normally".

Another home I visited has a gardening group who look after an allotment in its grounds. Most of the group are male and not only enjoy doing something practical, growing vegetables and plants, but having a natter and putting the world to rights. Another spin-off is that the produce they grow supplements the kitchen and reduces the running costs for the home.

When visiting a care home with a view to placing your loved one there, ask yourself the question, "Would I trust this care home to care for my loved one properly?"

Of course, care homes are regulated by the CQC, but in my experience and that of fellow carers, a high accreditation mark doesn't necessarily mean what it says. The CQC may have visited on a good day.

Having said all this, over the years, I did find a few care homes that I would trust to care for Barbara.

In July, Barbara had to stop involvement with WotsTots altogether, as her dementia had progressed to a point where she couldn't do her role properly. This was a sad day and the end of an era.

The leaders asked me if I was going to retire too. I said that I would carry on doing the refreshments, telling the story occasionally and singing, which would enable them to carry on doing what they were there for, talking with and interacting with the mums and children.

In August, we went to Essex to have a pub lunch with Barbara's three sisters Irene, Kath and Gill. They were finding living with Barbara's dementia very difficult because, as their eldest sister, Barbara had been heavily involved in their childhood and upbringing.

At the Carers Group, Sally introduced us to the "This is Me" initiative.

This is a document produced by the Alzheimer's Society. It contains a photograph of the person with dementia, along with relevant information that would be useful to a carer or medical professional treating them either at work (care setting), in the event of a home visit by paramedics, or in hospital. We created one for Barbara and kept it by the front door, so that it was handy if and when one of these people needed to see it.

Bristol Brunel Lions also supply (free of charge) their Green Bottle scheme, which is very similar. Relevant information is written onto a document, which is the placed in a green and white plastic bottle which is placed in the fridge. A sticky label with a green cross is placed on the front door of the property for any visiting professionals to see and recognise. The label signals that there is relevant personal information in the bottle in the fridge.

2012: Olympic Year and Barbara becomes a "Hugger"

This was the year of the London Olympics! The whole country was very excited to be the host this time.

One of the important lessons I had learnt was to complete a Lasting Power of Attorney (LPA) whilst the person with dementia has the capacity to do so. Fortunately, Barbara was still able to understand what they were, as we been executors of the will for her dad, so I downloaded the forms from the Office of the Public Guardian, assembled all the relevant people in our lounge one afternoon and completed them.

There are two LPAs:

- Finance & Property,
- Health and Wellbeing.

It's very important to complete both of these documents early, they prevent a lot of problems later on as the dementia progresses. Barbara and I had often talked about our LPA, so I knew exactly what her wishes were.

A will is also very important whilst the person has capacity, again, it prevents a lot of arguments and heartache later.

With Barbara now attending The Limes regularly, I was able to spend some time to do a few things independently without having to worry about leaving her in the house, whilst I worked on the car or garden for example.

Meanwhile her dementia had progressed to the stage whereby she hugged and kissed everyone, even total strangers! It got a bit embarrassing at times, particularly in supermarkets and shops, but everyone loved her as she raised the mood and gave people a smile.

An example of this was when we went to our regular local supermarket. I was putting our shopping in the trolley only to turn round and see Barbara in a big embrace with a strange man. He shouted out, "Who is this woman?" I intervened and apologised say,

"I'm sorry about this, she has dementia and wants to smile and hug everybody." He calmed down and understood. We chaps aren't used to women throwing themselves at us! However, passers-by thought it quite amusing.

This was an example of what Frontal Temporal Dementia is, the brain cells at the front of the brain affect personality and behaviour. It had certainly affected Barbara in this way, she had never been a "hugger" with total strangers in the past, and she had only smiled at people when appropriate to do so.

People with dementia can also be affected by obsessive compulsive disorder (OCD). Barbara would always insist that we bought three loaves of bread when doing our weekly shop. We don't eat three loaves of bread a week! So, when shopping, I would buy three loaves this week, use one, put two in the freezer and not buy any more for a couple of weeks. To me, it looked like she had OCD.

On another occasion when I was doing the housework, I went into our bedroom to make the bed and there was an awful smell on her side of the bed. I traced it to her wardrobe and when I opened the door, what did I find? A loaf of bread! It had been there for some time and had gone mouldy, so I threw it away into the rubbish. But I know what she was thinking. "We mustn't run out of bread", so she put a loaf in the wardrobe. We don't keep bread in the wardrobe, do we? We keep it in the breadbin.

I have heard similar stories where women have put their underwear in the fridge. There is a book written called "Knickers in the Fridge" written by Jane Grierson, whose mother has Alzheimer's Disease, which talks about this.

Is this OCD or general confusion?

On another occasion, we got up one morning and I went downstairs to begin breakfast. When Barbara came down, she had her T-shirt on over her jumper and looked like Wonder Woman. I took her back to the bedroom and we put them on properly and in the right order.

Another incident I remember is where I had gone downstairs to start breakfast. Barbara came down a few minutes later.

On entering the kitchen, she asked, "Where's my mum?"

Well, her mum had died decades before, but it would serve no purpose in me telling her that. Telling someone with dementia that a loved one has died can start the whole grieving process all over again.

Thinking on the spot, I said, "Oh, it's alright Barb, your mum's at work, she'll be home later."

She replied, "Oh, OK", and carried on as though nothing had happened.

Some people would say that this is lying, but I don't believe I was lying. I think she probably had a dream during the night about her mum and expected to see her in the kitchen when she came downstairs. Because I was there, she asked "Where's my mum?" Due to me responding with something that was quite normal to her, she passed it off, not raising it again.

I had entered her world in that moment because she couldn't enter mine. The lesson is don't argue, live in their world for that particular instant.

Another incident occurred when she went for a walk without me being aware. It was a lovely sunny evening, and I was mowing the grass in the back garden. Barbara was sitting in her chair on the patio. I'd cut half of the grass and Barbara was still in her chair. I carried on cutting the other half and had my back to her. After a couple of minutes, I turned round and realised she wasn't there.

I ran indoors to see where she was. I looked in the lounge, kitchen, toilet, upstairs and downstairs, she was nowhere to be seen. I went back into the garden and realised the back gate was open. I rushed out into the street. Our road is quite short, there are only fourteen houses in it, but I couldn't see her. She couldn't have gone far; she was in her chair a few minutes before.

I jumped into the car and drove around the block, no sign of her. Panic was now beginning to overtake me.

I was just about to start a second wider search when my mobile phone rang. On answering it, a male voice said, "Is that Mr. Hall?"

My reply was, "Yes, it is."

The voice said, "We think we've got your wife at our house."

I said that she'd disappeared from home a few minutes ago and asked where he lived. It turned out to be just round the corner on the main road. I drove round to the house to find Barbara with a man and his two daughters.

What was Barbara doing?

Smiling and hugging them as though there was nothing wrong!

I apologised to them for the inconvenience and asked what had happened. Apparently, Barbara had walked into the university grounds (which is why I didn't see her when I drove around the block) and had been picked up by another man, who brought her to the house where this man and his daughters lived.

I asked how he knew my mobile number.

He replied that she had her handbag with her (fortunately she takes it everywhere) and when they looked inside, they found her diary with my mobile number in it.

I apologised to them once again and we all had a good laugh as it turned out OK in the end, fortunately!

I was retelling this story to one of the mums at WotsTots and she asked if I was on social media. I replied that I was. She said that if I "friended" her and it happened again, I could message her and she could let nearly two thousand people in her young families group know. They could search near where they live, so in a very short space of time, a huge crowd could begin a search. This appeared to me to be good use of social media!

Barbara and I had never been to Ireland, but in June we booked a week-long coach trip with our long-standing friends Ray & Doreen. The tour started in Birmingham, where our feeder coach linked up to the main touring coach and we set off to Ireland via Holyhead. We visited various places as we toured clockwise in the Republic and then entered Northern Ireland. Barbara coped very well with the journey and tourist sites. Fellow passengers were very kind when they realised Barbara had dementia. Barbara particularly enjoyed the Irish dancing - as in Riverdance - which seemed to be the main attraction at most pubs. My sides were aching when I got home from laughing so much. The Irish people are friendly, funny and very welcoming.

We were enjoying our newfound friendships with those that attended the day centre and our walking group. On a fine day in June, Hilary, one of our friends, arranged to have a BBQ in her garden, which was a lovely occasion.

Some of our folks had lost their husbands and partners, so those in this position had formed a group called the Graduates (because they had moved on from being carers, they had "graduated") and arranged regular lunches to which I was invited (although Barbara was still very much alive). We also had a Christmas meal together.

There was not much going on for young people of working age with dementia. A fortunate meeting with Anne from the Alzheimer's Society led to us being invited to a new Young People's Dementia Group. (We were still under seventy remember!).

This was really helpful, as we met with people of our own generation, plus some who were still working. We were able to talk about common issues like our favourite songs, groups and music, sport and so on. We talked about singers and groups of our era rather than Vera Lynn (nothing wrong with Vera Lynn of course if you're from that generation!). Those attending were a mixture of carers, people with dementia and professionals.

Young people with dementia who were still working had a whole different set of issues to deal with from those older folk who had retired. For example:

- Were they still able to cope with their job effectively?
- Would they be able to keep their job?
- If they lost their job, who would pay the mortgage/rent?

Two guys attending the group were forty and forty-four, living with dementia and still working with the support of their employers.

There was lovely story we heard about later involving a national supermarket and a lady employee who had developed dementia. Over a period of five years, she was moved from one job to another within her capability, until she finally had to be medically retired,. But that woman had the support of her manager and colleagues for five years. Wonderful!

It is very easy to write off people with dementia from the workplace. There was an initiative in Bristol a few years later called "The restaurant that makes mistakes". It was led by a Michelin starred chef, Josh Egerton, who recruited people of all ages with dementia to set up and run a restaurant. All the roles were covered by people with dementia. Barbara and I were invited to attend. To say it was brilliant is an understatement. I chatted to a few of these folks and asked one male waiter what he thought about working in a restaurant.

He replied joyfully, "I feel useful again. Life is worth living. I'm making a contribution."

This man had previously been a director in a manufacturing company.

In September, I met up again with my three walking buddies to walk part of the Severn Way from Shrewsbury to Upton-on-Severn over seven days.

We now called ourselves "The Last of the Summer Wine Ramblers", because on a previous walk to Hadrian's Wall, we were sitting with our backs to the wall eating our lunch, when a groups of lady walkers passed by. They laughed as they saw us and said that we reminded them of "Compo, Cleggy and co". The name stuck and caused great amusement among our friends.

Our four wives met us to have a celebration finishing meal. Barbara travelled up with my eldest daughter and was very glad to see me.

2013: The Launch of Bristol Dementia Action Alliance (BDAA)

In January, I was offered a second day per week at The Limes for Barbara.

Barbara's care was coordinated through Care Direct at Social Services, via Bristol City Council. I rang them straight away, and they agreed to finance it, as Barbara's care package was quite small. Barbara started the following week, although she didn't want to go, she wanted to be with me. However the staff really made her welcome and she became one of "Claire's Team". She again asked if I had enough petrol to go back and collect her, and told me not to cross any roads without looking! All anxiety based.

With Barbara now at The Limes two days a week, I offered to do maths as well as listening to the children read at school. So I helped Julia, the Special Educational Needs Coordinator (SENCO), run a maths group on Fridays.

Another note in my diary recorded that on a local walk up to The Downs, we were passed by an ambulance sounding its siren. Barbara started to cry because she said that people were hurting. It seemed amazing to me that her dementia had increased her sensitivity, not just to the noise of the siren, but to what it meant, someone needed medical help.

As well as the good times, there were also some not so good and embarrassing ones. One such occasion was the funeral of one of our Drop-In friends at Canford Crematorium. A funeral was already in progress when we arrived, so we were invited to wait in the entrance hall. While we were waiting, Barbara suddenly decided she was going to go into the service in progress. I was talking to one of the assembled groups, and turned round just as she burst through the door into the service. I grabbed hold of her arm just before she could sit down, apologised to the assembled congregation, and took her out. Embarrassment is an understatement.

I received an invitation to the Drop-In's 10th anniversary tea, but I didn't tell Barbara, as she would have wanted to come with me instead of attending The Limes. That would have set a precedent and I would have had a problem getting her to go to there again. She was very anxious about what I was doing and whether I was doing anything special and to take care crossing the roads.

Barbara's need for personal care was also increasing. A lady called Anita offered to come to cut Barbara's toenails. Barbara wouldn't let me do them, no way! As the dementia increased, however, I did take over her personal care, washing and styling her hair (which I felt quite proud about), dressing her, changing and washing her as she became incontinent. I did, however, take her to the hairdresser regularly to have it done professionally and keep her to the standard to which she was accustomed!

There was also a need to buy her clothes and I remember one instance where I needed to buy her a new bra. I wanted to make sure I got the correct one of the right size, and I went to a well-known national store that I knew had a bra measuring service. I know I could have looked at the size of her existing bras, but I wanted to make sure I did it right.

I'd never bought Barbara's underclothes before and, like a lot of other guys of my generation, approached the two ladies offering this service with a little apprehension. No need to worry though and they were lovely and recommended products in similar style to the ones Barbara normally bought.

There was an incident when one of our grandsons came to our house and saw her produce a pool of urine under the table whilst she was doing her jigsaw. He was obviously quite shocked at this experience and came running to tell me what had happened. I often wonder what effect Barbara's dementia has had on my children and grandchildren. Children shouldn't have to witness this.

I said to my children that my grandchildren have lost their Nanny. As a mother, grandmother and nursery nurse, she had so much to offer them. It's tragic to me that all that has been lost. It's an awful disease. My children, being adults, dealt with it in different ways, but they were all grieving for their Mum. They were suffering bereavement although Barbara was still physically around.

One evening I heard Barbara laughing in the bathroom. She was standing in front of the mirror and laughing at her reflection. I think she thought she was engaged in a discussion with somebody, not recognising that the reflection she saw was herself.

Mirrors can be quite deceiving and confusing for people with dementia, as on another occasion I noticed Barbara looking in the mirror in our lounge, first at the mirror, then at the reflection of walls and door, back to the mirror etc. She went from mirror to wall trying to work out why she could see both. This continued for what seemed like a couple of minutes. I realised she couldn't understand that the door was real, and the mirror reflected the image of the door. In the end, I changed the mirror to a picture to avoid confusing her, as pictures are not reflective.

At the young people's group, Anne told us about a guy in Torquay called Norman McNamara who had recently co-founded the Purple Angel Campaign. He had spoken at an Alzheimer's Society event which she had attended. Mike and Lynn had also heard him and thought he was brilliant. "Norrms", as he likes to be known, has had Lewy Body Dementia since 2011/12. He was Chair of Torquay Dementia Action Alliance. He had recently begun to raise awareness of Dementia in Torbay, following an unfortunate incident in a supermarket, by delivering information sheets to businesses in his local high street.

I thought this would be a good person to meet and talk with about raising dementia awareness in Bristol. We arranged a visit to see Norrms and his wife Elaine at their home in Torquay. This meeting proved to be life-changing for Barbara and me. They were such an inspirational couple and told us what they were doing locally, and they suggested we started a DAA (Dementia Action Alliance) in Bristol too. We finished our meeting with me saying to them, "Well it has been great meeting and talking with you both. What you can do in Torquay, we can do in Bristol."

We asked our church if we could hold a meeting. They agreed and on 9th July 2013 we held a public meeting entitled "Is Bristol a Dementia Friendly City?" Invitations were sent to all the agencies we knew about that were involved with carers and people living with dementia locally e.g. Alzheimer's Society, fellow carers and people we knew from the Drop-In, our carers support group and young people with dementia group. We discussed what was available in the city and how dementia awareness was being progressed. There was a lot going on, but as always, there were gaps, and more could be done.

That day, Bristol Dementia Action Alliance (BDAA) was born and launched with me as the Chair.

The following morning, I found an envelope in my porch with £50 in it to set us on our way! So, we had £50, a blank sheet of paper, no charity (or any other) status and an objective, which became our vision statement, to:

"Make Bristol THE Dementia Friendly City of the UK."

Easy really isn't it, we just had to change the thinking, behaviour, and culture of 500,000 people, but...

"He who aims at nothing hits it!"

Our vision was to create a city where people with dementia would be treated with common courtesy and respect. Kindness costs nothing.

Our values were set:

1. We believe that people with dementia have the right to a good quality of life and to remain independent in their local community.
2. We believe that people with dementia have the right to live well, engage in and contribute to their local communities as long as they wish to do so.
3. We will address negative attitudes and raise awareness and understanding of dementia.

We decided that we would increase awareness of dementia in businesses, schools, children's groups, clubs, community groups, faith groups - in fact anybody who would listen and engage. We were in the education business.

"Dementia has no boundaries and we're not going to create any."

(Not grammatically correct, but you get the idea!)

Our main messages were:

1. What is dementia?
2. What are the symptoms?
3. How can you support someone with dementia?

Education is key because:

We don't have "I've got dementia" tattooed on our forehead."

I'm not a doctor or a scientist, but BDAA is the only way I can cope and fight the dementia. I couldn't save Barbara from it, but I can fight for meaningful change, so that social care enables those we love to live well with dementia, not just in the future but now.

We started BDAA as a community action group, later becoming a registered charity. Being a registered charity gave us more "street cred" and we became accountable to The Charity Commission.

Our first activity was to form a group of volunteers and walk around our local high streets with Purple Angel Campaign information sheets on dementia. These were similar to the ones used by Norrms in Torquay. We talked to the managers of mainly small, independent businesses about becoming dementia friendly.

Lots of villages, towns and cities were beginning to form DAAs at this time and we attended several launch events in North Somerset, Devon and Cornwall. At one such event, we met the other co-founder of the Purple Angel Campaign, Jane Moore.

With the launch of BDAA, I left the carers support group which was now being led by two new workers. Barbara's dementia was getting worse, albeit at a gradual pace, and she couldn't be left alone.

In September, we went on holiday to Bude in Cornwall with friends of ours from church, Jeremy and Heather. I remember this trip this because one day we decided to hire a rowing boat on the canal. Heather was quite surprised at the thought of Barbara getting into a rowing boat with her dementia, but she managed very well, and we really enjoyed a good time. A great holiday.

In October, BDAA decided to run a Dementia Roadshow in East Bristol. We were over the moon as over thirty people attended, so we decided to run another one in South Bristol. This one was equally well attended, with Norrms being our main speaker. This again received positive feedback, so we organised another one in North Bristol.

Having started BDAA and visiting Norrms, I wanted to become an ambassador for the Purple Angel Campaign and increase dementia awareness. In November, Norrms arranged a meeting in a Paignton hotel with fifty of us meeting as the original Purple Angel Ambassadors. An ambassador from Germany, Martina, had flown over and stayed with us so that she could attend. The campaign was becoming more international.

2014: Is Bristol a Dementia Friendly City?

January saw our first dementia awareness session with a Brownie Pack. Our church has two groups and Julie invited me to her group which met on Tuesday evenings. Having worked with children for most of my life, I found this a great opportunity. After giving them a bit of basic information about dementia, most of the "learning" from the evening was achieved through role play and a quiz. Being Brownies, they also received a badge, an information sheet for their parents and a group certificate confirming that they were now our first "Dementia Aware Brownie Pack".

A few weeks later, I'd heard that the Alzheimer's Society had initiated a "Dementia Friends" programme, so I attended a session to become a Dementia Friends Champion. As a Champion, I could now offer Dementia Friends sessions as well as those under the Purple Angel banner.

Bristol DAA now had two tools with which to increase dementia awareness, the Purple Angel Campaign and Dementia Friends.

I was still listening to children read and helping with maths at our local primary school, Elmea, when Julia, the SENCO, and I talked about the school becoming dementia friendly. The result was that we ran three dementia awareness workshops with the year six classes and did a drama at assembly. Elmlea became our first Dementia Aware School and has run sessions every year since.

Cooperation and partnership between embryo Dementia Action Alliances (DAAs) were starting as well. We shared our little experience with each other and strived to encourage and support each other.

"Dementia Day on the Buses" was the title given to a joint initiative between South Gloucestershire DAA, Bristol DAA and FirstBus. It was held at the bus garage in Easton, with FirstBus providing a single decker bus in the carpark and the DAAs providing a group of people with dementia and their carers. We had invited them to demonstrate the problems they encountered with buses.

One of the outcomes of this day was the setting up by the two DAAs of the Avon and Somerset Dementia Forum (ASDF). DAAs were being launched all over the country and it was felt that we could meet every two or three months to see what each was doing, support and encourage one another.

We also set up a page on social media, so that DAAs could keep in touch and report events they were running virtually.

I was also asked to run a dementia session for Action for the Blind. A couple of days before the event, I realised that of course some of the attendees would have visual problems, preventing me from running the session as I normally would. I decided that it still needed to be interactive, so I told them on arrival of my dilemma and asked if they would mind working in pairs, one with visual issues and one without. They thanked me for considering the issue of visual impairment and the session went really well with everybody engaged and positive.

An invitation was also received to run a dementia awareness session for volunteers at our local hospice, St. Peter's. About 40 people attended, but it seemed quite strange to be talking to volunteers supporting terminally ill patients, some of whom may have had dementia, as they were doing this regularly. Feedback though was very positive and further sessions followed.

Later that year, we received an invitation to attend our niece's wedding in Ireland. This involved flying to Cork from Bristol. I don't know how easy you find moving through the airport process, but unless you are a frequent flyer, it can be a nightmare. Imagine what it's like for someone with dementia or a carer.

Firstly, you arrive at check-in and hand over your papers. The lovely lady deals with these, gives you the tickets and says, "12 o'clock, Gate 3."

So, the first question is "Where's Gate 3"?

Well at Bristol, it's upstairs. So how do you get upstairs, where's the stairs, escalator or lift? Wouldn't it be useful to have coloured lines or footprints from each check-in desk to a common line leading to the lift, stairs and escalator? All the check in person would have to do then was to say "12pm Gate 3, follow the footprints/coloured line to the stairs, lift or escalator". Some Bristol hospitals have this arrangement, and it works well.

Having arrived upstairs, the next challenge is moving through security. Emptying your pockets into a tray, removing your coat and belt is OK, but then Security then asks you to take off your shoes.

Barbara kicks at this, "What have I got to take my shoes off for?"

Security begins to explain, but at this point I step in and say, "Excuse me, but she's got dementia. Can you look her in the eyes, speak to her very slowly and tell her exactly what you would like her to do." Meanwhile the queue gets longer!

Security understands, and we eventually move on through the process.

But of course, this charade takes place at every point you present your papers, passport, boarding card etc until you sit in your seat on the plane. It repeats itself at your destination and also on the return journey.

Totally frustrated at this, I was determined to contact the airport on my return about becoming a Dementia Friendly airport. From a BDAA point of view, if we could get the airport to be dementia friendly, we would really take off!

The wedding itself was lovely; a moving ceremony, photos in the park and a boat trip. However, we did experience an incident with Barbara and her wine at the wedding breakfast. As everyone knows, it's a sin to have an empty glass in Ireland! Our waiter kept filling Barbara's glass up with wine, despite me telling him not to and taking it away from her. Naturally, the obvious result ensued with her being sick all over the tablecloth and her jacket.

On our return to Bristol, I contacted the airport asking if I could go and talk with someone about them becoming Dementia Friendly. The first thing they said was that we weren't their charity of the year that year, so they couldn't help. I replied that we were not asking for money, we wanted to have a conversation about them becoming a Dementia Friendly airport. Cutting a long story very short, we eventually had the meeting and we have been working together ever since. One of the things they asked us for is a "one page jogger" that they could give to their customer-facing staff.

We have been involved with the airport quite a lot since and publicised their initiative on TV demonstrating how they cater for non-visual disabilities, like dementia, as well as visual ones.

Living life at 100 mph didn't stop, as we were informed that our grandson Josh and his girlfriend Amie had given birth to a baby girl called Amelia. We dashed up to Scotland, but I was quite shocked at Barbara's reaction to the baby. On arrival, Amie gave her to Barbara, who cuddled her for about two minutes and then handed her back. This was not the Barbara we all knew, and I felt sorry for all of them, so I held her for a long time. It wasn't the same though!

One day, I received a call from Jenny at the BBC. She'd heard about BDAA and wanted to run a programme for Inside Out West on dementia. She wondered if she could centre it following Barbara's and my journey. So, we were interviewed at our house, at Singing for the Brain, on our daily walk on The Downs and at The Limes. We were also interviewed at a Worcester garden centre with Alistair Burns, NHS England's National Clinical Director for Dementia.

Dementia awareness sessions were beginning to step up as well. We visited South Gloocestershire memory social workers, Tesco, the Care Forum, a group of councillors at Bristol City Council, Trinity Road Police Station and some prospective MPs standing for the upcoming election. I even gave a dementia friends session to two candidates in a pub!

I was also being invited to speak about dementia and caring for someone with the condition at carers groups. I also heard about a monthly carers group for men run by the Carers Support Centre called "Pie n a Pint" at the Willy Wicket pub. It was an opportunity to socialise with other guys and I found it useful on the couple of occasions that I managed to get there.

2015: Happy Days are Here Again

When Barbara was first diagnosed, I felt like my whole world was falling apart. Everything that I knew about the disease was based on (frequently inaccurate) media representations. Alzheimer's Society became my go-to resource for quality, accurate information on Alzheimer's care and family support resources.

A partnership between the Alzheimer's Society and NHS Devon had recently seen the introduction of a new service for people with dementia and their carers called the Dementia Wellbeing Service (DWS). This service has professional medics and Alzheimer's Society staff working alongside each other and is unique to Bristol. We have since suggested to our CCG (Clinical Commissioning Group) that they standardise it across the three areas of the CCG.

People with dementia and their carers are generally referred to DWS by their GP (or they can self-refer). DWS would then allocate a "Navigator" who becomes their single point of contact throughout the whole process until end of life. This is music to the ears of carers, and why we suggested they standardise across the CCG, as prior to this, the question was asked:

- do I contact the GP?
- do I ring the Memory Clinic?
- do I contact Care Direct?
- who do I ring?

Very often, you would ring all of them and be passed from pillar to post! All the carer needed to do now was contact their Navigator and he/she would arrange whatever was needed, be it a clinical issue, Care Direct issue, or social activity (clubs, groups etc) issue. We were allocated a Navigator called Vicky to navigate us through our journey.

BDAA, still being very young, wanted to build relationships with all agencies supporting people with dementia and their carers to see how we could work together, and I was very kindly invited to the initial Navigator training session and team meetings.

One Saturday morning, Barbara was doing her jigsaw puzzle and I was doing some work on the computer. We had our backs to each other. Suddenly there was an enormous crash and I realised she'd fallen off her chair and lay frightened on the floor. I reassured her that everything was OK and gently tried to see if she had broken any bones. After confirming that she hadn't, I manage to get her off the floor and onto a chair. Again, I tried to reassure her that everything was OK. Then I noticed she had blood in her hair and investigation proved that she had a cut. I quickly treated this with a dry pad and then gave her a cup of sweet tea as she was still in shock. All the time I was wondering what had caused her to fall off her chair in the first place. Did she fall asleep, had she fainted, or did she have a mini stroke? I thought she needed to go to A&E to get checked out. I rang my eldest daughter who confirmed that that was the best thing to do and off we went to Southmead Hospital.

At the hospital, we were treated like royalty. We were in A&E for four hours with scans, ECG and lots of other tests being carried out. Fourteen medics of one specialism or another saw her! The result was inconclusive with nothing being found apart from the cut.

Three months later, she collapsed on the floor again.

This time, we all agreed that she must have had a mini stroke. I also made sure her chair had arms on it. We learn by our mistakes!

At BDAA, we were often asked where our funds came from, to which we would reply, "The generosity of the British public". However, a friend of ours, Peter, led a choir called the Harlequins Singers and they very wonderfully arranged a concert at our church to support us and raise some funds.

Our church was very good with Barbara. She smiled at everyone and tried for a hug, which some were only too pleased to oblige! During the service, she would sometimes start laughing just at the moment the minister was delivering their punch line. Thinking about how our church family were very accepting of Barbara's change in personality and behaviour, we thought it would be useful to share our experience of what churches should and shouldn't do with people living with dementia. Therefore, we contacted several agencies in our increasing network, as well as several churches, and began to think how we could run a "How to be a Dementia Friendly Church" event. This proved to be very well received and those attending took the ideas and suggestions back to their churches. This has since become an annual event and a resource pack produced which can be found on the BDAA website.

We had opened a café at Westbury Baptist Church to serve the community. I asked if phase two of this initiative could be the setting up of a Memory Café for people with dementia and their carers. Although we had ideas of our own, the café manager, Linda, and I thought it would be useful if we visited other memory cafés to see what they were offering. On 24th March, one such café we visited was at Thornbury. We were very impressed with it and utilised some of their ideas into ours:

- Warm welcome from volunteers (not just the heating)
- Name tags for all
- Information table
- Memory table
- Items and pamphlets on the table to stimulate discussion.

(There is now an item on the BDAA website called "Tony's Top Ten Tips for setting up a Memory Café")

Another project we initiated as BDAA was "How to be a Dementia Friendly GP Surgery". You would think that GP surgeries are dementia friendly, wouldn't you? But thinking about it, the doctors receive training in dementia, sometimes the nurses do, but who's the first person you speak to - the receptionist, who thinks they're trained because they can diagnose you over the phone!

We contacted every surgery in Bristol offering to run a dementia awareness session. Out of the 70 practices in Bristol, we've helped 17 become dementia friendly.

A problem for most Community Action Groups, of which we were one, is raising funds. Funders generally ask for a charity number, but these are only offered to registered charities. We approached an organisation in Bristol called Voscur, who supports the voluntary sector. A lady called Kate took us through the process of applying for charity status.

I never dreamed that I would be taking Barbara to the toilet and changing her! However, in July, Barbara wet the bed...Twice! She also wet herself at The Limes. Toileting was now becoming a big issue as Barbara was becoming incontinent, so I ordered two twin beds. Incontinence progresses and of course she later became doubly incontinent.

Being over 50, she was also invited to the Breast Screening Centre for a check-up as part of the national initiative to diagnose breast cancer early. This visit turned out to be an absolute hoot. On arrival, we walked up to the receptionist with her appointment papers. The young lady reached out for the paper and Barbara leaned forward to hug her. This brought shock to the receptionist and some amusement to other staff and patients waiting. She dealt with it very professionally, took the paper and advised us to take a seat.

Her name was called a few minutes later and we were led to see two medics for the check-up. Because of her dementia, I was asked if I wanted to stay and help take her top and bra off. When asked to rest her breast on the machine, she again started laughing and reached out to hug one of the women.

Eventually, she complied and put her breast on top of the plate.

In order to take a picture of course, she had to remain still.

No chance!

She reached out to hug them again. One of the ladies suggested they turn the plate 90 degrees and take a side print. After several attempts at getting a photo, one of the nurses suggested the check-up be abandoned, which it was.

I got Barbara dressed again and as we were leaving, Barbara was still smiling at the staff and trying to hug them. She eventually said goodbye and they all smiled at her and said, "Thank you for coming here today, Barbara, you've made our day!"

So, living with someone with dementia isn't all doom and gloom!

September saw us celebrate our 50th wedding anniversary with a big party. It was great to see friends from far and near that we hadn't seen for years and of course, they were all sad to see how Barbara had deteriorated from the person they once knew.

Also, I had always wanted to go to the Isle of Man. Our long-term friends, Ray and Doreen, once again offered to take me for a week's respite, Barbara being looked after by our children. A lovely time.

Following our visits to several memory cafés earlier in the year, we held a training day for volunteers to discuss how we were going to operate our café at Westbury Baptist Church. We would run it on the first Friday of the month from 2pm to 4pm. It needed a name, what were we going to call it? Various suggestions were made, but we eventually opted for Happy Days - suggested by Steve from church. We believe people with dementia can look back to happy days, have happy days now and still look forward to happy days. They are still members of the family and community; they are just ill!

On the first Friday of November, we all arrived, everything was ready for a 2pm start. All we needed now was people to come along. At 1.50pm two arrived, at 1.55pm two more arrived and by 2.10pm eight people had come along. We were off!

Our theme tune was the Happy Days theme song from the American sit-com, and it was opened by "The Fonz" (i.e. me dressed up). Our plan was to have fun as well as provide information, the opportunity to talk and the opportunity to laugh. Various performers, activity leaders and organisations were invited along to lead some of the sessions, but our main thrust was to have fun as well as be serious. Laughter is the best medicine, so we were silly for two hours.

It became apparent very early on not to call Happy Days a memory café to people with dementia. It is a memory café, but these folk don't want to be reminded of their condition, a little respite is good for everyone. We also learnt very quickly not to use the word "dementia" or "memory problems" as these terms could turn the conversation in an instant and the whole conversation could be lost. So, we invited people to Happy Days and aimed to give them some fun.

As well as serving tea, coffee and home-made cakes, our volunteers were also asked to talk to the people with dementia, as well as the carer. Very often, people with dementia are isolated because they are left out of the conversation. For example, we ask the carer, "Would he like a cup of tea or coffee?" rather than asking the individual. Depending on which phase of their dementia journey they're on, they might not respond to a choice question anyway, it may be more productive to say, "I'm having a cup of tea, would you like one?", then they can respond with a "Yes" or "No".

"There is more to the person than the dementia" is one of the lines from Dementia Friends. I attended a course run by Alive Activities on how we can engage people with dementia in conversation using digital devices like a tablet or laptop. For example, you may be trying to talk to an elderly man who has dementia. The questions asked may follow this pattern:

- What did you do for a job?
- Oh, you were in the military, were you?
- Which arm of the military were you in?
- You were in the navy, which ship did you sail in?
- HMS Gloucester?
- You can then get a photo of HMS Gloucester up on the tablet.
- What can you tell me about your time on HMS Gloucester?
- Which ports in the world did you stop at?
- Gibraltar?
- What did you do in Gibraltar?
- You now have built the basis of a conversation and you can communicate!

2016: BDAA Becomes a Registered Charity

I've mentioned care homes before and the year began with BDAA being invited to a local one to run a Dementia Friends session for the staff, carers, volunteers and the families. It went really well, and we were asked to run another two.

We were also being invited to lots of childrens and young people groups e.g. Explorers/Rangers, Scouts/Guides, Cubs/Brownies, Beavers/Rainbows, Air Cadets, St John's Ambulance, to name but a few. Children are curious and do not hesitate to ask the difficult questions. Two questions regularly asked are:

1. Can you catch dementia?

No, you can't. You catch a cold, or catch a ball, but you can't catch dementia.

2. Can children get dementia?

I have heard of a handful of cases where children have had symptoms similar to dementia, but this is extremely rare. When a child asks me this question, my reply is "Yes, but it's extremely unlikely that you will get dementia as a child." That I believe to be the truth.

Over the past two years BDAA had applied to become a formal registered charity, trained our steering group (trustees) with Voscur, and in May 2016 we became a registered Charitable Incorporated Organisation (CIO). We were now recognisable and accountable.

Life was becoming busier and busier, including arranging lots of activities as part of Dementia Awareness Week. We ran a few Dementia Friends sessions, helped Zion Café in preparation for the setting up of their memory café, supported follow-up Dementia Friendly Church events at Sea Mills and Trowbridge and also visited the local community centre at Avonmouth.

If we were to enable Bristol to become a Dementia Friendly City, we had to get politicians involved. So I asked if I could attend some Neighbourhood Partnership meetings to let them know what our aim was and how we needed their support. Some locals became interested and Dementia Friends sessions followed as a result.

One such group was Henleaze Townswomen's Guild. Following their session, they asked what they could do to support us. We replied that it would be great if they could help us make all the shops and businesses in Henleaze dementia aware. This was achieved by giving them a little bit of training, ordering some more of our booklets "A Guide to Understanding Dementia" and then asking Guild members to visit all the premises in the main streets during Dementia Action Week next year, 2017. They were keen to do this.

Another target of our activities was the football and rugby clubs, Bristol City, Bristol Rovers and Bristol Bears. City and Bears play at Ashton Gate which is a new stadium with increased capacity. We were invited to run some Dementia Friends sessions there and to give a view on how dementia friendly the new stadium was.

Later we were invited to run some sessions for the National Citizens Service (NCS) by Youth Moves. We ran these for four years running and the students graduated at a ceremony at Ashton Gate, to which we were invited.

From being a children's and youth worker for many years, I was very happy to talk to groups in which they were involved. I ran dementia awareness sessions for St Christopher's Scouts, Westbury Baptist Cubs and Chew Magna Guides and Brownies. (Chew Magna is not in Bristol, but there was no DAA there, so I went).

A Dementia Friends session was also held at Greenway Health Centre which was very well received and became a regular event, as their staff changed regularly.

A local radio station in Bristol has a lunchtime programme called "Babbers", this being a local colloquialism with Bristolians saying, "Alright me babber" to each other. Barbara and I were invited along to speak about our situation. Barbara became the star of the show.

One of the habits Barbara formed was to gnash her teeth. Although she was seeing the dentist regularly, I asked the dentist if a gum-shield might help. She had one made, but of course Barbara didn't like it at all and took it straight out again. Perseverance was required, but Barbara still hated it and would hide it in her pocket. One day, I found it down the back of the sofa. Then it disappeared altogether. A couple of days later I saw it in the gutter in a nearby street!

On another occasion, I was working on my computer and Barbara was doing her puzzle. Suddenly, I heard her laughing. She had picked up the photo of our four children, taken when they were really young. She kissed each child in the photo. I don't know if she kissed them because she recognised them as our children, or just because they were children. I guess I'll never know.

Barbara's vocabulary was also changing, for example, I'd say "I love you", she'd reply "I like you"!

She was also repeating herself quite a lot.

We were in the supermarket one day doing our weekly shop when we bumped into a lad I was listening to read at school. He said, "Hello Tony", to which his mum said in a protective manner "Who's that?" He told her that I listened to him read at school and she relaxed. However, Barbara would always repeat this story, so much so that our grandchildren could recite it word for word.

Every parent and grandparent is proud of their children and offers support and encouragement in their development. One day we were privileged to go to London to see our grandson Jacob play piano with his school music group at the "Actors Church" in Covent Garden. He had a small part to play, but we were very proud of him.

I had another visit to London again in October, when my children treated me to a "Legends Tour" of the Emirates Stadium. As an Arsenal fan, I was over the moon that we would be taken round by one of my favourite players and a true footballing legend, Charlie George.

One event we always looked forward to was the annual BRACE Dementia Research charity conference in November. This year was special as Adam, one of our trustees, was one of the speakers.

In September, Ray and Doreen took me to Cornwall for a

week's respite. A friend at church had recommended a good care home to look after for Barbara whilst I was away. My children were now finding it difficult to physically move Barbara and care for her properly.

I visited and it looked good, a modern building with seemingly good facilities and activities, they even had a hairdresser come in once a week. It cost quite a lot, but if they would care for Barbara as they said they would, it would be money well spent. To my mind I trusted this home to care for my wife.

When I went to pick her up on my return from respite, my heart sank as soon as I saw her. I said to myself, "Oh my giddy aunt Barb, what I have I done to you?"

She was sitting in the common room, looking really fed up. Her hair had been combed back with no style, and she look ten years older than she was.

I asked how she had been during the week and was told that she'd "been fine". What does that mean? I expected more and asked about her activity, whether she'd had her hair done as suggested, but it seemed as though I was being fobbed off.

A staff member took me to the bedroom so that I could pack Barbara's clothes. I took the case from on top of the wardrobe, where I had placed it the week before. The staff member just threw the clothes into the case instead of folding them neatly first.

Personally speaking, again, I expected more, she didn't seem interested and most people I know fold clothes neatly before packing them.

I just got the impression that the staff just wanted to get rid of us.

Bearing in mind that this home had been recommended to me by a friend, and all the formalities before Barbara's stay were very cordial, helpful and friendly, my expectation of the care to be provided was that it would be excellent. Sadly, it wasn't the case from our experience.

Other than putting her in a place where I had expected them to care for her, I had done nothing wrong, but I still felt guilty placing her there. This resulted in me writing a letter to the manager expressing my disgust. (See Appendix 1).

I realise this is just one example of one care home, but it certainly confirmed my view of care homes at the time. I have visited other care homes since and they all vary, but the question to ask yourself is, "Can I trust the people here to care for my loved one?" It's care you're paying for, person centred care!

As a result of sending the letter, I was invited in to see the regional manager. We went through my letter paragraph by paragraph and discussed each point. She said that she was very sorry that these things had occurred and that I had to write a letter of complaint. Various things would be taken up with appropriate staff and training would be reviewed.

I replied that she could do whatever she liked, but Barbara would never stay in her home, or any other home belonging to that group, ever again.

2017: Recognition and Awards

At Elmlea school, where I supported maths and reading, Julia the SENCO was retiring. Her replacement was a teacher named Vicky. On discussing the dementia awareness sessions being offered to children's groups, Vicky asked if I could run one at her daughter's Rainbow group. I replied, "Absolutely, just ask the Rainbow Guider and if she agrees, let me have a convenient date."

The session was held, and all the girls thoroughly enjoyed it.

Later that night, I had a phone call from Vicky saying what a great time her daughter had had. When she got home she sat her mum, dad and sister down and gave them a "lecture" on how dementia is a disease of the brain, and that when we see people having problems with their money at the supermarket checkout, they may have dementia and we needed to be kind and offer help instead of moaning. Basically, she told them all the things she'd learnt that evening through our talk and roleplay. She also gave them our leaflet to read and showed off her new "Dementia Aware" badge.

What's the old saying, "Out of the mouths of babes..."

Vicky was really taken aback by how much her daughter had taken in. She and the Guider recommended the session to the District Commissioner for Girlguiding, Maria, who ran groups at Totterdown.

I put a post on my Facebook page which read:

> In these modern times when all we seem to hear about is doom and gloom, it is really refreshing to have some good news to share.
>
> You may remember I posted an item about being asked to run a Dementia Awareness session with St. Bon's Rainbows. As a result of that session, I was asked to run a similar session for the Rainbow unit run by the Bristol & South Glos County Commissioner, Maria. As a result of that session, Maria invited

me to run a session with her Guides the following Tuesday. Barbara came to this one with me and I set her up doing her jigsaw puzzle, whilst I ran the workshop. At the end of the evening, two young guides brought Barbara a cup of tea and two biscuits. I had told the group earlier that Barbara is at the stage where she hugs everyone. After receiving the tea and biscuits, she gave the girls a hug! A few more guides and guiders went to talk to Barbara and of course she hugged them too. I've realised that this is a brilliant illustration of inclusion, Barbara may have dementia, but she is still included.

Following this, Maria emailed all her guiders recommending they find a slot in their programme to include our dementia awareness session. This is now happening and I'm passing all the S. Glos ones onto Winsome at S Glos DAA.

As a consequence, Barbara and I attended Westbury Baptist Rainbows and had a similar evening to the one with Maria's Guides. Anyway, last Thursday, I was given a carrier bag of things from our church children's worker, Zoe, who said "This is from Helen, the Rainbow Guider." Inside were four children's puzzles similar to the one Barbara had done at their group. There was also a big, home-made "Thank You" card which the girls had made. At the top was a big THANK YOU and underneath was a picture of Barbara doing her puzzle. Inside were lots of individual notes from the girls thanking us for teaching them a bit about dementia. I was beginning to well up reading it. There's a lot wrong with our world, but there are still a lot of kind and caring people around aren't there?

In March, we held our now annual "How to be a Dementia Friendly Church" event at Westbury Baptist Church. Although we were meeting and discussing these issues as Christians, dementia affects everyone regardless of faith or ethnicity. Also Bristol is a diverse city with many faiths, languages and ethnicities, so we shared our increasing knowledge and experience with the multi-Faith Forum and different cultures.

We held several dementia events at All Saints Clifton, Bristol Old Vic, Skipton Building Society, St Pauls Advice Centre and Windmill Hill City Farm. We also ran another one as a follow up for Henleaze Townswomen's Guild, who we had met the year before.

These "Guild" ladies were still very positive about making Henleaze a Dementia Friendly community and were keen to visit all the high street shops and businesses.

We decided that, with Dementia Awareness Week coming up in May, it would be a good time to act, because the focus nationally would be on dementia. Several volunteers would visit all the businesses in the main roads with our BDAA materials. Every business took a "Guide" and they had no refusals.

The week actually started on the Friday with a Dementia Roadshow at St Peter's Church and ended with a jazz band event at Trinity URC on the following Saturday, with several other group activities arranged during the week.

I was looking for a place to go on holiday, when a friend suggested a dementia friendly venue in Devon. It was a bungalow in Topsham, near Exeter, and was run by a nurse, Sallie. Also, next door, she led a day centre for people with dementia and Barbara could attend three days a week. We could spend the other days together visiting places, having a ride on a steam train, enjoying a cream tea and so on. As it was a three-bedroomed bungalow, we also took a friend Dilys with us to give her a break, and also to thank her for looking after Barbara whilst I ran our dementia awareness sessions.

The holiday worked well, and Barbara was well looked after and enjoyed being fussed over, so much so that we booked again for the following year!

In July, Julia formally retired from Elmlea school, and I attended her farewell party. I was now helping Vicky with the maths group of children.

Through working with Youth Moves, we were invited to run more Dementia Friends sessions for teenagers under the

National Citizens Service (NCS). Having left school, these young people embarked on a three-week event to learn skills to become better citizens in the community. As well as outdoor pursuits like abseiling, orienteering etc, they learnt such things as teamwork, communication skills, financial management and so on. They also had visits from local charities to learn what they were doing in the community and were also given the opportunity to do some work for them. BDAA was one such charity.

As well as running Happy Days memory café, we were also interested in other cafés either running or being set up within the city. We were still an embryo café but were keen to see what others were doing. One such café was the one being run by Rachel and Sue at the main Bristol hospital, the BRI. It was great to compare our experiences and we went on supporting each other, with the café using some of our BDAA materials for those that were interested. A regular supply of our information was available in the potting shed in the hospital's garden as well!

Hospital visits for Barbara were still the name of the game as in July she had an appointment with the stroke clinic. In September it was the podiatry clinic at Hampton House Cotham for foot problems, her left foot was beginning to look like "crows foot".

Following our holiday in May at Topsham, we decided that we would have another break there in September, this time going with our long-standing friends Ray and Doreen.

My family and friends had been suggesting for months that I could really use a cleaner to help in the house, so in October I took on a woman called Shannon who cleaned a couple of hours a week for me. This prevented the house becoming a "man pad"!

Barbara hadn't spoken a word for months. One morning in October, when I dropped Barbara off at The Limes, Barbara suddenly said "goodbye" as I left. Claire and I raised our eyebrows, looked at each other in surprise and said to each other, "Did she really say that?" She was still smiling at everyone, and we called her "Smiler". Everyone loved her.

Although dementia causes heartache and pain, there are also some humorous times too. I remember one such event.

At 11am on the dot every morning, people at The Limes went to the site café. On this occasion everyone sat at their tables for their usual mid-morning coffee.

A chap on a neighbouring table had ordered tea and toast. When Barbara saw his toast arrive, she thought "That's nice" and reached out and took a slice. Everyone laughed, including the guy whose toast it was. One of the staff apologised and told him that she had dementia, but I reckon he'd already guessed that.

One Sunday morning in church, Barbara looked at me and was rubbing her fingers. She seemed anxious as though she was trying to tell me something, I then noticed she wasn't wearing her wedding ring. I had a quick look around but couldn't see it anywhere. After the service, several people helped us, but we didn't find it. Maybe she'd lost it on the way to church or at home?

We retraced the path to church and did an extensive search at home, but still didn't find it. I reported it to our church caretaker too, just in case she found it when doing the cleaning.

This incident really upset me, because we think her engagement ring had been stolen years ago by a child we had fostered, and now her wedding ring had been lost. What I couldn't understand is, she'd never taken it off since the day I put it on her finger in church when we got married. Someone suggested I could buy her another one, but you can't replace a wedding ring, can you?

She had also started to fiddle with her earrings. One day I found that she had managed to take one off and was chewing it. From then on, I didn't put them on her when I got her washed and dressed in the morning. I didn't put her watch on her either for the same reason, she might take it off and chew it or lose it.

One Thursday morning as I was getting Barbara ready to go to The Limes, she had great difficulty going down the stairs. She seemed frightened. I managed to get her down and onto a wheelchair that a friend had given me.

On my return from dropping Barbara off at The Limes, I realised that this could become a real problem and that we needed a stair-lift quickly. So, I rang a company I found on the internet, explained the situation and the lady said she could send a surveyor to the house at 10 o'clock that morning. Brilliant!

He arrived on the dot and measured up and asked when we would like it installed. I explained what had happened and he said, "How about next Monday morning?" I couldn't believe it. We camped out upstairs for the weekend and the stair-lift was installed on Monday.

At a meeting with Adam, our BDAA Treasurer, he invited me to a dinner that he and his wife were attending. It would be a good opportunity to "network". He said that it wasn't a black-tie event, just suits and tie. As the day drew nearer, I became more and more suspicious about this event, something didn't quite add up. Then I got the message that it was a black-tie event. Something was going on that I knew nothing about.

The dinner was scheduled for 25th October, and I arranged for our friend Dilys to sit with Barbara. My daughter gave me a lift to the venue, so that I could have a drink (or two!). I arranged for her to pick me up at 9.30pm, so that it wouldn't be a late night for Dilys.

I wasn't aware at the time, but Adam and John from BDAA had nominated me for the Outstanding Achievement Award at the Bristol Health Awards.

I arrived at the venue early and saw that all the tables were set out for the dinner. There were ten people allocated to each table with nameplates provided. I was handed a programme and taken to table number one. I became even more suspicious! Looking at the programme, the names of the winners for the various categories were named, although the one for the Outstanding Achievement Award just read, "to be announced". I relaxed somewhat.

The guests arrived, with Adam and Fiona joining me on table one.

It had been decided that four awards would be awarded before dinner and the remainder after dinner. I told Adam that I was being picked up at 9.30pm. As they started handing out the first four awards, it was announced that five awards were now going to be presented before dinner, including the Outstanding Achievement Award. I became semi suspicious again.

You've probably realised quicker than I did, that I was the winner of the Outstanding Achievement Award! The actual award wsa presented to me by Care UK.

I didn't realise how naive I'd been!

Sitting at home one day having a cup of tea, my solace was interrupted by the phone ringing. On answering it, a lady called Carla, from a community trust, introduced herself and said that she had heard about BDAA and wanted to help us.

I said, "Brilliant, how would you like to help?"

She said that she had just become a Dementia Friend, looked at our website and liked what we were trying to do. She wanted the trust to give us a grant, a substantial grant at that, and it was over three years!

I said that if she was going to give us that sort of money, then we would use it on a project and that I would have to speak to our steering group/trustees. When asked for suggestions on what we should do with the money, they suggested employing a part-time assistant to help me as the Chair of the charity. I thought this was a great idea and we pursued it.

2018: Growth

The year started with our pantomime at Happy Days, "Little Red Riding Hood", performed by three professional actors who toured round care homes and memory cafés. It was brilliant. "Oh, yes it was!"

The joy was however short-lived as our next "event" was me attending the Royal United Hospital in Bath for a test in preparation for an operation on my left eye. I was petrified at the thought of the operation!

When I was seven years old, I'd had an operation at Moorfields in London on my eye to cure a squint. This event remained with me all my life and I was scared then as a child, even more so now I was an adult. Technology has moved on I know, but the thought of having someone operating on my eyes still filled me with dread.

My daughter had the day off and took me to Bath for the actual operation, whilst Barbara was cared for at home. However, I needn't have feared, once they gave me the anaesthetic, the next thing I remembered was coming round, operation complete and successful.

Following up on Carla's phone call before Christmas, we had received the first instalment of the grant. It had been agreed that I needed an assistant, so we advertised for one. Job interviews were held on 20th February and as a result, Sam started to work for us as our part-time employee. This was to prove to be one of the best decisions we ever made!

Although I had received a wheelchair from a friend, we had a formal occupational therapist (OT) assessment for an NHS one later that month. I didn't realise there is so much to consider in providing a wheelchair, however a new one was ordered of the correct size and dimensions.

Just prior to this, Barbara and I had been invited to All Saints Church in Winterbourne to talk to them about becoming a dementia friendly church. Halfway through the meeting, Barbara fell off a chair, bruised her forehead and had a small wound on her nose. We went to Southmead A&E where the nurse "glued it". We were treated like royalty and only had to wait 20 minutes.

Barbara had a good night, but I kept her home from The Limes so that she had a quiet day. It looked like she had a mild black eye!

In March, staff at The Limes were finding it difficult to cope with Barbara's mobility. An urgent request was sent by Jo, the manager, to Care Direct for a review. As a result, Barbara moved from The Limes to Bristol Community Links. Barbara's last day was a sad time with Suzanne, Jackie and Sarah at The Limes.

For years, my retirement plan was to become a Bristol Guide, showing people around the historic city. I find Bristol a fascinating city with a rich history. Over the years family and friends had bought me books and videos enabling me to learn more about Bristol's past. I practiced on friends and family coming for the weekend.

Caring for Barbara obviously influenced those plans, but an opportunity came up in May when the Walkfest Festival was arranged. I decided that I would organise a walk around the harbourside. With Barbara in a wheelchair, I designed a route which would take in a lot of attractions but would still be wheelchair friendly.

The Alzheimer's Society had brought in an initiative called "Singing for the Brain" and we attended a group in St. Monica's retirement village; however, our local Alzheimer's Society in Bristol had followed this with another brainwave called "Singing on the Train". Carers and people with dementia could have a ride on the train from Temple Meads to Seven Beach and return. During the time on the train, they would sing popular songs and have a quiz.

I wanted Barbara and me to join in with this and get involved, but wondered about parking arrangements at Temple Meads. I made some enquiries and discovered that I could drive to Sea Mills station, leave the car there, travel into Temple Meads with wheelchair assistance being provided on the train, meet the group and re-join the train. We could then enjoy the outing with the group and get off at Sea Mills on the return journey, pick up the car and drive home. A brilliant day, it went well with assistance provided by the guard for Barbara and her wheelchair being first class.

Another day, I received a phone call from Avon Fire and Rescue asking if we could help them in running Dementia Friends sessions for all their staff. We naturally agreed and ran sessions for the firefighters and admin staff in several stations. This was the start of a good working relationship between Avon Fire & Rescue and BDAA.

In June, we went for our second holiday to Topsham with Dilys. Barbara again attended the day centre and was made a fuss of and really welcomed.

In September we returned to Sallie's bungalow in Topsham, but this time with our long-standing friends Ray and Doreen. Barbara was now using a wheelchair and we'd managed to borrow one there, to save taking one in the car.

When using a wheelchair, your whole life changes. One of our day trips out was to the Dart Valley Railway running from Paignton to Dartmouth. The railway treated Barbara really well, proving wheelchair access to the carriage and allocated seats for the disabled. When we arrived at Kingswear, the ramp was again provided allowing us to get off the train by a very friendly guard. Our trip was across the River Dart to Dartmouth. In order to get her onto the ferry, four of us had to lift Barbara and her chair onto the boat. She wasn't able to walk on at that time and it was easier to lift her in the chair.

Once in Dartmouth, we discovered the streets are cobbled, an uncomfortable ride for a wheelchair user. There are no sloped pavements, an issue for the carer pushing the wheelchair.

Another major issue for a carer is family support.

Caring can be, and often is, very tiring, particularly as the condition progresses. This means that support from family and friends is crucial to the carer, otherwise they become worn out. I have a friend who is a busy director of a company, but he still visits his mum in a care home three times a week. Another friend has a father with dementia, she and her sister visit three times a week on a rota system. I know other families where nobody visits, the nearest family live two hundred miles away.

Another issue raised by many carers I've met is that you don't get invited to family or friends' events anymore, for example barbeques. This may lead to feelings of abandonment, because those inviting don't know what to say or do. The stigma and embarrassment of dementia remains. Or they may be upset by the condition of the person with dementia, that they are not the person they used to be. This can lead to the carer being isolated, which in turn can lead to depression.

Whilst visiting another carers group, one of the speakers said, "If you can't visit when the loved one is alive, don't attend the funeral when they're gone. Isn't it interesting that family suddenly become interested at the funeral and reading of the will!"

A lot of truth in that, but it really does bring out the cynical thoughts in me!

Barbara and I had run dementia awareness sessions for lots of Girl Guide units and I was surprised to receive an email inviting us a presentation evening in September on the SS Great Britain, where we would both be given a Girlguiding "Thank you " award. This came as a big surprise, but was lovely.

This meant that I had to buy a new outfit for Barbara so that she looked "the business" on the night! She also wore her earrings and watch for that special occasion.

Also in September, I received an invitation to speak about dementia at a local Bristol school, QEH. This had come via a lad in our church who had been trying to get us to do this for years, but now that he had left to go to university, teachers had agreed. So, I led an assembly on a Friday which was a "Mufty Day" (pupils can wear ordinary clothes instead of school uniform, but they have to pay £2 for the privilege). The money received is given to a local charity, on this occasion it was for BDAA.

Through our "Being a Dementia Friendly Church" work, I received an invitation to be involved in a Dementia Friendly Church service in October at Trinity United Reformed Church in Henleaze, a privilege indeed.

We celebrated our third birthday for Happy Days memory café in November, with a wonderful cake made by Tina, who also led a pom-pom dancing session.

As well as Townswomen's Guilds, we were also being invited to other women's groups and in December we visited a large WI group in Blaise/Shirehampton. We were getting involved with lots of different groups in the city and increasing dementia awareness! Things were going in the right direction.

2019: Dementia progresses

An Occupational Therapist (OT) review in January suggested that Barbara should be provided with a hospital bed instead of her twin bed. I was a little hesitant in agreeing to this because it meant that she was moving on to the next stage. I suppose I was trying to fight the dementia.

To make life a little easier (and protect my back), Barbara was being moved around the house on wheels, we had a mobile commode upstairs, a wheelchair downstairs and a stair-lift between the two.

Barbara was having trouble with her eating, so I was spoon feeding her. To make it a little easier, I was feeding her easily digestible food like cottage pie and rice pudding. To help with her drinking, I put "Thick n Easy" in her drinks to avoid it coming out of her mouth.

People often commented on how well I was coping with Barbara's condition. I usually replied that I had my sad moments the same as everyone else. We are not made of stone; we are human beings. Some days I was overwhelmed with love for Barbara. I looked at her and compared the woman she was now to the woman she had been.

The Guides presentation evening at the SS Great Britain in February was a splendid occasion and Barbara looked lovely and she was again, totally spoilt. I had even made an appointment with the hairdresser to have a special hairdo for the event.

Barbara had lost her wedding ring, so I bought her a ring to wear on her wedding finger with other rings I had bought her over the years.

In February, we at BDAA were very surprised, and delighted, to receive a request from Linkage, a charity for the over 50s. They wanted us to run two half-day training sessions for people who were working, or wanted to work, in the community with people with dementia and their carers. This proved to be beneficial to us and our attendees because we learned a lot from putting a three-hour training package together and the attendees were able to share their experiences and learn from each other.

As a result of these two workshops, we were asked to run eight more over the next few months. Bearing in mind that we were working with all communities in Bristol, we invited Asian, Black and other ethnically diverse representatives to attend as well. This proved to be really positive, and they took their learning back to their communities.

Transferring Barbara from her wheelchair to the toilet had become difficult and the day centre, Bristol Community Links (BCL), had been using a sling to do this. When we booked our now regular holiday with Dilys to go to Topsham, Sallie asked if her carers could borrow the sling from BCL. This was agreed. We had discussed using a hoist and sling at home with an OT, but for various reasons it was not practical at that time.

We used the sling again when we visited Topsham again in September with Ray and Doreen.

In November, we celebrated our fourth birthday for Happy Days memory café. A birthday party is not the same unless we have children there, so I invited our local nursery to send their children and staff. They agreed. We provided the food, little sandwiches, jelly and ice cream and they arranged the games.

For some time now, Stokeleigh Care Home had been bringing a group along to Happy Days and we discovered that one of their ladies, Myra, had just celebrated her 104th birthday! We thought it would be a great idea to ask her to blow the candles out (not 104, just four, otherwise we might have caused an energy crisis!). We sang happy birthday to Happy Days and then to Myra and she did blow the candles out. But of course, the children wanted to blow out the candles too, so we let them all have a go at doing that.

Myra was chuffed, so was Stokeleigh, so were our regulars! This proved to be a great opportunity to bring four generations together and mixing at the party. We would do this again.

We were giving talks on dementia to lots of groups now and one such group was Stockwood Ladies Group. They had decided that we would be their "Charity of the year". We gave the talk and, naturally, Barbara was the star of the show with everyone making a fuss of her. People are so kind.

There is tremendous power in music as we all know. You can listen to a song or a piece of music and instantly you are taken back to an occasion from long ago when you met someone, were at a wedding or a celebration. This has great value for someone with dementia because it stimulates their memory.

We had heard about, and positively encouraged, two initiatives, Playlist for Life and the Purple Angel's initiative of giving out MP3 players to people with dementia free of charge.

We had placed MP3 players in a local hospital and several care homes. We needed to know the name of the recipient, 15 to 20 of their favourite songs and an address to send the player to. All we required in return was feedback, so that we could supply positive evidence of their value when applying for funds.

We supplied some MP3 players for the Chinese community. A lady gave us the playlist of 20 songs but, of course, she wanted them in Chinese! I sent the list off to Steve our technical expert saying, "Here's a challenge for you pal, this lady wants these songs, but in Chinese, what's the chances?"

I assume there's a Chinese version of Spotify, because he came up with goods and the lady was over the moon! So were the Chinese community, so much so, that two more ladies with dementia asked if they could have one.

A great result and an example of reaching all communities.

Another initiative promoting music was Playlist for Life (PFL), which encouraged people to create a playlist for someone with dementia on their own digital devices (laptops, tablets etc).

PFL was looking to set up help points across the country. So we arranged a training day at Bristol Community Links. This resulted in Claire constructing a playlist for Barbara.

When we were at home, we would listen to Radio 2 and very

often I would sing and dance to the songs being played. Barbara would look at me, smile and start laughing. Most people laugh when they hear me sing!

As you read this book, it may seem that I am jumping from one subject to another, however, this was how life was turning out. One minute I would be caring for Barbara, the next I would be dealing with BDAA activity. Who says men can't multi-task!

2020: Covid 19 Strikes

January got off to a good start for BDAA, as we were nominated for (and won) the Resilience Award at Voscur's Bristol's Social Impact Awards. Voscur is an organisation in Bristol that supports the voluntary sector.

Then, shortly after, we were hit with the Covid 19 pandemic. The world was turned upside down and in March the UK government put the country into "lockdown". People were told to stay at home to save the NHS from being overwhelmed. This meant that the day centre temporarily closed, "Singing for the Brain" went online, and Happy Days stopped because the church building where we met was closed. We learnt the importance of washing our hands, wearing a mask and keeping two metres apart from each other (known as social distancing), well most of us did!

We were advised to shield vulnerable relatives and loved ones, so I kept Barbara at home just before the day centre formally closed. I did jigsaw puzzles with her, and we watched YouTube songs and videos.

It certainly had a dramatic effect on Barbara's world. All her outings including the day centre, "Singing for the Brain" and Happy Days obviously had to close face to face activity. She became very clingy; we didn't go out of the house for three weeks. However, I decided to reclaim my garden and grow some vegetables, so I planted potatoes, tomatoes, broad beans, runner beans, leeks and carrots.

Although the day centre was closed, we did receive weekly phone calls from Wendy to see how we were coping.

"Singing for the Brain" went virtual and was hosted on Zoom, but Barbara couldn't cope with it because there was no action on screen, and she lost interest after 30 seconds.

At Happy Days café, we asked the volunteers to phone our regulars weekly to make sure they were OK, had all their basic food and supplies met and, very importantly, to have a chat. At least they had some contact with the outside world!

Like many other communities, we also formed a WhatsApp group with the other residents living in our road. We were able to care for each other by ensuring everyone had contact, their basic needs met and an opportunity to chat. Neighbours were extremely kind to Barbara and me because of her dementia and offered to do our shopping. Lots of people went online to do theirs, but one of our daughters did ours.

One neighbour celebrated his 90th birthday, so we gathered at his front gate and sang "Happy Birthday" to him (socially distanced of course!). He had a birthday cake, and another neighbour gave him and his wife a bottle of prosecco. Lovely!

We were also asked to support the NHS by going out into the street at 8pm every Thursday and clapping our hands. This was great and often neighbours chatted well after the clapping stopped.

On 8th May, the country celebrated the 75th anniversary of VE Day. Everyone in our street met outside, some bringing tea and cake, others bringing something a bit stronger! We went out at 3pm and didn't go indoors again until 6.45pm!

Also in May, we set up a fortnightly teleconference for Happy Days folk with Alive Activities. This was because some older people don't have a computer, laptop, tablet, or smartphone (and don't necessarily want one!), but they do have a telephone (which they know how to use).

We also arranged some activities on Facebook and Zoom for those who did have digital devices.

The first teleconference was led by Nikki and took the form of a reminiscence hour. We were asked to remember what games we played at school as children. I recalled my primary school, which was located next to the Robertson's jam factory, so there was always a smell of jam. They also had an air raid siren signalling lunchtime (I think it was 12.30 or 1pm). Popular games when I was at primary school were marbles, hopscotch, conkers and kiss-chase!

Barbara was still very clingy, and I wondered what I could do about it. I'd heard about a therapeutic doll called Emily (she does have a lot of brothers and sisters too). So, I sent off for Emily and gave it to Barbara, particularly when I had to go out of the room. She would cradle Emily in her arms and "talk" to her like a mum talking to her toddler. She looked quite at ease as she had done this for years.

Our holiday plans had to be cancelled at the end of May too. I had contacted Sallie in Topsham as normal to make a booking, but, due to Covid restrictions, she wasn't allowed to rent the bungalow out for holidaymakers and was also forced to close the day centre. Later, she decided to rent her bungalow out as a normal rented property. I hope it reopens one day, as this was the only dementia friendly holiday of its type that we knew about.

In July, although the day centre in Bristol was still closed, two ladies were sent round to the house one day a week to take Barbara out for an hour to give her some fresh air and allow me some respite. I was told that they queued up to do this because everybody loved her. The centre did reopen again in August, and I was invited to take Barbara in for one day a week, later to be increased to two.

For some time, I had been having difficulties in getting Barbara in and out of our car. Our family and friends had been warning me for some time that I could do myself an injury and really hurt my back, so, in August I bought a Wheelchair Adjusted Vehicle (WAV). It was brilliant because I could keep Barbara in the wheelchair and take her from the house, down the ramp into the front garden, along the path, straight into the back of the car. Much easier on the back!

This particularly pleased our occupational therapist (OT) who visited soon after for a review. She also wanted to change Barbara's wheelchair, saying it was now too big and was preventing her sitting upright. I told her that I was having problems washing Barbara and I may have to think about giving her a bed bath at some stage. She said that the first step was to provide specialised bedsheets, she also warned that bed-baths required two people, so I would need to think about additional help from a second carer!

Barbara was also having problems eating and drinking and it

was recommended that I contact the Speech and Language Team (S<) to make an assessment. Due to Covid restrictions, this was carried out virtually with a lady called Sophie, who monitored me giving Barbara her lunch. I gave her shepherd's pie. Sophie liked this and told me to carry on giving her this easily digestible (minced) and moist food. An alternative could be fish pie.

She also agreed that Barbara ate and drank better when she was upright and held her head slightly back, as she did in our reclining chair.

Barbara had started making a groaning/growling sound during the day. It was intermittent, she didn't do it all the time, but then she started doing it at night, waking me up in the process. After a little while, I decided to move into the back bedroom. Disrupted sleep could cause problems for me, as well as my care for Barbara.

Our Dementia Wellbeing Service (DWS) Navigator, Gaby, contacted me for a review and I updated her on our situation. Barbara was sometimes waking me up three, four or five times a night, leaving me exhausted in the morning.

Later in the year, we heard of the sad death of Barbara Windsor. This very popular actress of the "Carry On" films and "EastEnders" had developed dementia a few years ago and had been cared for by her husband Scott. I actually met Scott at an Alzheimer's Society Awards event in London, and we compared notes on our "Barbaras" over lunch.

Dementia generates such embarrassment and shame, and we need to bring it into the open and treat it as just another condition. We must find a cure for it. If we can find a cure for Covid 19 in months, why can't we find a cure for dementia? Like Covid, dementia has no discrimination, it doesn't care about your background. We need a cure and for that we need money and the willpower to find it! Please help fund the research required.

We also need to accept all folk with visual and non-visual disabilities as a normal part of society. These people don't ask to have the conditions they have, it is not a matter of choice. Improvements have been made since the 2012 Paralympic Games held in London, but we need to keep up, or increase, the momentum.

We're still learning the lessons of Covid too. It feels to me that when the pandemic hit the UK, several mistakes were made.

- The Covid 19 pandemic was not taken seriously until the first lockdown on 23rd March.
- People with dementia were removed from hospitals and moved into care homes allegedly without being tested.
- This had a devastating effect on care homes, particularly those with residents with dementia.
- More than a quarter of those who died in England and Wales had dementia.
- Family and carers were refused access to them and had to talk through the windows in the garden.
- People living with dementia and their families were the hardest hit by the pandemic. People with dementia didn't understand why their loved ones didn't visit, they felt abandoned and heartbroken. Of course, their loved ones were trying every way they could to visit and were heartbroken also.

Christmas time was fast approaching, and I was sad not to be putting on the big red suit at Avon Valley Railway due to the Covid restrictions. However, I was really cheered up on receiving a Christmas card from Ros, a family friend who used to work with Barbara and the children. It read:

> Thinking about memories and people special to me. Barbara encouraged me and believed in me, to train as a Brownie Guider and then to take over from her as Brown Owl. It was a happy time together and I will always be grateful. Then we worked together at Christchurch with the pre-school for some years. I remember it so well, I remember saying to her, I will never remember all their names. She said, "yes you will", and she was right, I did. Happy times, happy memories, so thank you Barbara, you helped me to believe in myself.

This made me remember another lady Louise, with whom Barbara worked at Christchurch Pre-School. She had remarked to me years ago, "If a child was crying or upset, you'd just take them to Barbara, and they would be fine within a minute or two."

This is quite ironic, Barbara giving confidence to other women like this, because she also sometimes lacked confidence in herself. She was perfectly capable of course, but like a lot of girls and women I've met over the years, she lacked confidence in herself.

2021: Eating and Drinking Problems

The year started well with an invitation to join a virtual carers support group run by Louise and Wendy, Navigators from DWS. This was great because I'd got to know them over the years, and they knew all about our situation. These virtual groups had great value in the pandemic, as they allowed carers to let off steam and share their experiences and frustrations, even though they couldn't meet face to face.

One morning, Claire, who had created a playlist of Barbara's favourite songs whilst she was at the day centre at Bristol Community Links, rang to review Barbara's care package. Due to Covid, she had been reassigned to a different role within the Social Services part of the Council. From our discussion, I mentioned that I was thinking of getting some additional help at home in the mornings to assist me with getting Barbara up, washed and dressed. She thought this was a good idea, so I approached a care agency resulting in Julie and Michelle starting on 25th January. They were great and really took a shine to Barbara. I also asked for, and received, a third day at the day centre, which was another great help.

In February, Barbara was now having problems with swallowing. When I put food into her mouth, it seemed as though her brain was saying, "OK, you filled me up with food, what do you want me to do with it now?" Instead of swallowing it, she pushed the food out again. I poked it back in with my finger and eventually she swallowed it. I didn't expect Michelle, Julie and the day centre carers to do this though!

One Tuesday Michelle and I weighed Barbara, she was eight and a half stone. Usually, she weighs around ten to ten and a half stone! We contacted our Navigator Gaby and the Speech & Language Team to let them know what was happening and what we were doing.

Over the next few weeks, I started to spoon-feed Barbara her meals. Sometimes she ate them, sometimes she ate half of them, but she always ate her cornflakes at breakfast. I gave her cornflakes because the milk made them moist and easily digestible.

If she didn't eat her dinner, I gave her puddings and custard for tea. Crumbles, jam-roly-poly and sticky-toffee pudding (not all at the same time) with custard proved to be a winner and she just woolfed it down, no problem. I wasn't sure if it was because she was hungry, or had developed a sweet tooth, as some people do as they grow older.

Towards the end of January, Barbara and I had been called to have our first Covid jab (AstraZeneca) at the Greenway Centre. We had our second on 14 April, and were now fully protected!

Like many others, I was concerned that a quarter of care home staff nationally had still not been vaccinated and yet they were dealing with vulnerable people. Also, visiting arrangements were inconsistent, with some being allowed to visit and talking through the window from the garden, whilst others were not being allowed visitors at all. To me this inconsistency was an awful disgrace, especially as people with dementia couldn't understand this.

I wrote to our local MP to express my alarm. His reply reiterated my view, but as an opposition politician, he and his colleagues could only voice their concern, the power still lay with the governing party.

I was now sleeping in the back bedroom because Barbara was waking me up in the night with an intermittent groaning noise. One night, she didn't make any noise and I slept through the night. When I did wake up, the house seemed eerily quiet. You could have heard a pin drop, there wasn't even any traffic noise, there was not a sound. The thought flashed through my mind "Is she OK, has she died?" Horrible thought really! I rushed into her bedroom in a panic, and she was breathing normally with her mouth open. But of course, the thought stayed with me for ages. I asked myself what would I do practically in the event of her dying? Do I ring our GP, 999 or 111? Various people I've spoken to since say the GP, but others say whichever one of the three that you choose, it will be dealt with quickly.

I attended a webinar later that month on "End of Life" (EOL) where we discussed the importance of some very complex issues requiring sensitive handling, for example:

- Completing Power of Attorney (POA) whilst the person with dementia still has capacity.
- There are two POAs, one covers property and finance and the other health and wellbeing.
- POAs can prevent a lot of stress should the individual go into hospital for treatment for example, a major issue being whether they are seen as a DNR (Do Not Resuscitate) case.
- The advice is to start the EOL discussion early and write them into the POAs.
- Completing a will also prevents lots of arguments (and potential court cases) when the person finally dies.
- Considering the right time to place the person in a care home. This is fraught with problems for the carer/family, three major issues being the feeling of guilt for the carer, the cost and who is going to pay for the care?
- Considering the issue "Are we extending life or extending death?" We obviously don't want our loved one to die, but neither do we want them to suffer.
- People generally prefer to die in their own homes.

Another big issue when living with someone who has dementia is birthdays.

- Should we buy a card, or a present?
- Do they know who we are?
- They may ask, "Why are you giving me a present?"
- Should we invite them to the party?

My view, and yours may differ, is that for the price of a card, I would send it anyway. The modern approach is to send texts or put a post on social media, but I am "old school" and think it is much better to send a card. Some people say, well the recipient can't necessarily read or appreciate the card or the present anyway, so why bother? But I believe cards bring a lot more joy, particularly to older people.

There's a story told about an 80 year old man who used to visit his wife in hospital every morning. His wife had dementia and he was asked, "Why do you visit your wife every morning when she doesn't know who you are?" His reply was, "She may not remember who I am, but I know who she is!"

Weddings, wedding breakfasts, receptions, parties and family events can also be a nightmare, both for those sending the invitation and those receiving them. Of course, a lot depends at what stage the dementia is at the time. It's a progressive disease and gets worse in the individual over many years.

For the person sending invitations, issues are:

- Should I invite the person with dementia?
- Will I be embarrassed to have the person with dementia at my wedding or party?
- Will they "kick off" and ruin the occasion?
- Can they cope with things like loud music for example?

For the person/people receiving the invitation, issues include:

- For example, a couple where one partner is invited and the other isn't. The question of why may bring up a feeling of resentment that one half has been invited and the other hasn't.
- If the partner who has been invited decides to attend, this may bring about a feeling of guilt that the other partner will be left with a carer. Is that right?

So, there is a broader picture and a discussion required between the invitee and the invited which could prevent confusion, stress, hurt and misunderstanding. Hopefully a satisfactory answer for all concerned! For weddings, we must remember that the wedding is the bride and groom's big day, not ours.

Some other tips I received from attending a communication webinar:

- Body language says a lot more than your speech. People with dementia may not be able to speak any longer, but your body language tells them whether you're treating them kindly or not!
- The person with dementia may revert to their mother tongue. I know a German lady who had lived in the UK for years and spoke English well, but as her dementia progressed, she reverted to German, her mother tongue.
- Chunking i.e. asking a question with multiple answers e.g., "Would you like tea, coffee or a cold drink?" Ask one simple question e.g. "I'm having a cup of tea; would you like one?"
- In your conversation, don't leave someone with dementia "hanging", bring a conclusion to the topic under discussion.

In March, I had another visit from the Speech and Language Team, who suggested I construct and use regular diet sheets.

Over the years of going to our GP surgery, we had built up a lovely relationship with a woman at the pharmacy on the same site. In the early days, Barbara had always smiled at her and wanted a hug, so whenever I went to the pharmacy, this lady would ask how Barbara was. She was quite shocked at the deterioration, but always had a kind word and smile when she saw her.

Life is full of surprises and one day I received an email from our Rainbow Guider at church. Barbara and I had run a dementia awareness session for her group a couple of years earlier. The email said that she was now teaching in an English-speaking school in Luxembourg and asked if I could run a similar session for her class as part of the mental illness was part of their curriculum. Everything is done over Zoom/Teams these days and of course distance doesn't matter, so I agreed.

The session went better than I expected, and I was asked to repeat it for the Danish class. My Danish is non-existent, so they agreed I could do it in English! Again, it was well received, and I ended up running four sessions in total, so there is now a dementia aware school in Luxembourg. I didn't realise Bristol was so big!

Covid restrictions had prevented people from going out and doing normal activities like having your hair done. I'd managed to secure an appointment for Barbara just after the salon had opened and she looked lovely because of the stylist Caroline's work. Much better than when I did it!

Soon after we were walking around Westbury-on-Trym and the park on our daily walk, when we bumped into Sue and Richard from church. How nice it was to have a conversation with real people face to face after being confined to our homes for 23 hours a day. The conversation ended just as the village "chippy" opened. Perfect!

Often, when on our daily walk around the park, we would stop at the children's playground. As a nursery nurse and someone who had worked with children all her life, Barbara loved to see the children playing.

Sometimes, for our daily exercise, I would take Barbara to Severn Beach in the car. We would walk along the promenade towards the Prince of Wales Bridge, which carries the M4 motorway. This was a useful walk for me, as the tarmac is a wheelchair-friendly surface and provided a welcome change from our local walks around the village and Downs.

In April, following another visit from the S< team regarding Barbara's problems with eating, drinking and swallowing, I thought that I ought to keep an eye on her food intake. She was definitely losing weight. So, one of our carers and I weighed her on our bathroom scales:

27th April	8 stone	Checking her BMI on the internet, Barbara was the lower side of healthy for her age, gender and height.
5th May	8 stone 12lb	Weighed at the day centre. An increase!

7th May	6 stone 7lb	Were our bathroom scales accurate or was Barbara not standing on it properly?
26th May	8 stone 4lbs	Weighed at the day centre. Our scales not accurate!
27th May		Review Barbara's wellbeing plan with our DWS Navigator

To ensure that Barbara was getting enough vitamins, I was recommended to give her Fortisip drinks and puddings. I bought a couple at our local pharmacy to try them out and Barbara seemed to like them.

Late one afternoon, I received a call from our surgery asking if I could take Barbara in the following morning. This was for our GP to conduct Barbara's annual dementia review. I agreed. The receptionist then asked if I would mind if some medical students could observe the interview. I had no problem with that, we've all got to learn, plus it was a great opportunity to take our BDAA booklets and materials in for them! We can't miss an opportunity like that and so we killed two birds with one stone.

The review went well and at the end I was asked what one piece of advice I could give these medical students. I replied, "Listen to the carer as well as the person with dementia. The carer is usually the expert because they're coping with the situation 24/7. Their versions of what's going on may differ, but if you hear both sides, you can make a judgement call and make your own decision as to what's really going on."

For Dementia Action Week this year, the Alzheimer's Society brought in a campaign to "Cure the Care System". Governments of various colours have promised to address failings in the care system over decades. We're still waiting! In the run up to general elections we get fine words, but words are cheap, we need action!

Without pinpointing out any specific areas, my view is that the whole system needs reviewing and redesigning. Fellow carers and I have discussed this issue often and feel it is unsustainable as it currently stands.

People with dementia are stigmatised, ignored, isolated, and not supported. The system is inconsistent, and people are neglected. The little bit of support that is available, is generally aimed at retired people, whereas there are a significant number of people with young onset dementia (YOD) i.e. those of working age, for whom there is very little support.

In Bristol for example, 1000 of the 4500 of those living with dementia are people of working age. The issues facing young people with dementia are different from those who are retired. They may be anxious about job security, paying their mortgage/rent, the effect on their young children and not being able to pursue their hobbies or interests for example.

So, because support for those with YOD is sparse, we decided to do something about it. In March, with Covid restrictions still in place, we got a working group of interested people together over video conferencing. Our first idea was to create a YOD group on social media. We called it "The Denim Generation" at the suggestion of one of our YOD friends.

As Covid restrictions eased, we experimented by holding a face to face session with some YOD folk and their carers. It didn't really work, but we weren't giving up, perhaps it was still too early. As people became more confident in returning to normal after Covid, maybe they'd be willing to give it a try.

Another big issue is, should a diagnosis of dementia mean that you drain your savings? If you are rich or very poor, everything gets paid for. But if you have been prudent, sensible and saved over your lifetime, you pay for everything. Is that fair? Surely older people, who in the main have worked all their life and contributed to national taxes, ought to live their remaining years with their loved ones, without the stress the care system places on them.

"The true measure of society is found in the way it treats the most vulnerable."

As I have said before in this book, meeting socially with peers is really important for carers and people with dementia, it stimulates the brain. So I was really pleased to be invited to join a working group to set up a Meeting Centre in Bristol. The idea originated at the University of Worcester and interest has been growing all over the country.

Finding suitable venues in Bristol was tricky, as the centre needed to be somewhere "normal", where people usually meet, rather than a hospital, care home or place where people go for treatment or to be cared for.

We found a suitable place in Henleaze. It would be open three days a week (Monday, Tuesday and Wednesday), have some paid staff and volunteers.

Attendees would pay for attending, a bit like the system operated by The Limes.

I offered the landlord Dementia Friends sessions for his staff. If they were going to have people with dementia and their carers in their premises, they needed to know:

1. what dementia is
2. how to identify it
3. how to support and manage people.

On 2nd June Barbara celebrated her 75th birthday and the house looked like a flower shop, with blooms everywhere. She was totally spoilt and received soap, body cream, shortbread biscuits, a gift voucher for the hairdressers and a host of cards.

Happy Days restarted on 4th June with an outside café on the terrace at the front of Westbury Baptist Church. We were now known as "The church on the terrace". Sounds a bit posh to a working class "Cockney Sparra" like me. We had the statutory tea and cakes, as well as a catch-up. People were glad to meet face to face.

***

In June, I attended a couple of seminars to discuss care and support for carers.

Did you know:

1. Unpaid carers are saving the country £6 - 12 billion, depending on which journal you read.
2. The Carers Support Centre (CSC) provides training for carers (I have attended some as a carer for Barbara).
3. CSC arrange events for carers.
4. CSC chairs the Bristol Carers Voice. In my view, some of the professional bodies pay lip service to it, you're lucky to get the same representative turn up to two consecutive meetings! So, we provide our own support.
5. CSC, Dementia Wellbeing Service (DWS) and focus groups provide support by running carer support groups.
6. Memory Cafés provide respite for carers and people with dementia.

A Mini – Environment

It was around this time in 2021 that life was becoming very busy with caring for Barbara, being woken up during the night and also trying to keep BDAA running. As a result, focussing on this book became a low priority. I thought we were entering the final chapter, so the book went on the backburner, although I did make a note of some key dates and events.

On 25th June, an Occupational Therapist (OT) review recommended that we create a "mini - environment" for Barbara. This meant that she needed a hospital bed and hoist to lift her in and out of bed onto the wheelchair and/or commode. This was best placed in our front room downstairs, so a rapid rearrangement of furniture was made.

To enable this new situation, I also needed the help of a carer in the morning to help me get Barbara up, washed, dressed and breakfasted, and another one to help me get her washed and put to bed in the evening. A local care agency provided this extra help, and the carers were lovely.

Of course, the recurring question arose about this increased care i.e. "Who pays?"

So, the inevitable call to Care Direct (Social Services) was made to enquire. Fortunately, they agreed to pay for this extra care.

Caring for Barbara though was a privilege really. I knew that if it was the other way round, she would have done everything she could for me, but it was this way round, so get on with it!

During the day, I would look at her sitting in the wheelchair and I could see and feel the love in her blue eyes. She was my girl. She couldn't speak to me any longer, verbally that is, but she could communicate through her eyes and smile. I'd sing the song that was playing on the radio, or YouTube, and she would smile or laugh, and we'd pretend to dance. She enjoyed dancing.

With this new change however, I shared a "moment" with our

youngest daughter who phoned to see how I was coping. I shared that I was feeling really sorry for Barbara, she must be so frustrated.

My stoical, long-suffering, best friend and wife was deteriorating as each day passed. We believed in the common saying "use it or lose it" and Barbara was now losing the ability to do lots of things.

The hoist also meant no holidays. Even days out were a problem as a hoist was needed to take her to the toilet.

This disease had destroyed our family life.

Where we were once a very close family, with Barbara leading the way, family meetings were not like they used to be. Events might be unsuitable for Barbara to attend, and as a result I couldn't attend either as I'd be caring for Barbara. So, I was losing touch with my children, grandchildren and friends. I, too, was feeling isolated.

None of us could cope watching the woman at the centre of our lives gradually dying before our very eyes. This once really strong woman of principles and values was no more. She was now confined to a wheelchair and manoeuvred by a hoist. She was not eating or drinking properly.

Another day, Barbara wasn't herself at the day centre, carers said that she had been very quiet all day, she didn't seem herself.

I had a sleepless night wondering what the problem was with Barbara.

When our carer, Julie, arrived the next morning, I told her what had happened. We went in to wake Barbara up and she opened her eyes and gave a big smile. No temperature and being her normal self. We knew she was OK.

In July, we took our Happy Days folk to the dementia friendly allotment in Brentry.

The main objective of Happy Days is to have fun, so we were silly for two hours. I mean, what's the best medicine? It's humour and laughter, isn't it?

So, we try to give our folk a time of laughing because carers and people living with dementia need respite more than anything; we try to give it to them.

We also do a lot of singing because there's tremendous power in music. We don't need to have dementia to be able to listen to a song or piece of music and be taken back to a familiar memory. It may have been the first dance at our wedding, or a song from our favourite band etc, so for someone with memory issues or dementia it is very helpful.

We'd been involved in the early planning to provide a dementia friendly allotment, as a plot had become available at a local site and a friend of mine had floated the idea of making it suitable for people living with dementia. It was now being worked and managed by Alive Activities, another Bristol charity with whom we had close ties.

The site had been partially dug over, raised beds had been provided, it also had a shed and a toilet. A local builder had donated some paving slabs which were going to be placed around the plot's perimeter to make it wheelchair friendly. Barbara was the first wheelchair user to use it.

We'd invited a group of sea–shanty singers as entertainment. Two reasons for this: they didn't need electricity supply as there isn't one on an allotment, and they'd been recommended to us.

We also had a plant sale and a cream tea. We like cream teas; we are British after all!

The whole afternoon was a great success. Other plot holders on the site thought it a great idea to have a plot that was friendly to carers and people living with dementia. Now we need more across the city!

***

It may seem to readers that I was coping very well with caring for Barbara, but I'm as human as anybody else and have my moments. One such occasion occurred a couple of Sundays after the trip to the allotment. I tend to wear my heart on my sleeve, so I put a post on my personal social media page:

I can't cope any more. It's Sunday and I am in bits. After 20 years of caring for Barbara with her dementia, I'm at my wits' end.

For the last two hours, I've been trying to get Barbara to have some breakfast. I've managed to spoon-feed her a bowl of cornflakes, during which she went to sleep three times. She's also had the soft bit of half a slice of toast. I've also managed to spoon feed her a mug of tea.

Yesterday, she had a bowl of cornflakes, a yoghurt, and a banana (diced to enable her to swallow it). I did manage to get her to drink three drinks as I gave it to her via a spoon. This was all I could get her to eat and drink all day. She sleeps for twelve hours at night.

I'm really concerned that she doesn't eat or drink enough, even though I'm spending a lot of the day trying to get some nourishment into her. Needless to say, she's lost weight, she now weighs eight stone (112 lbs)!

People tell me how well I cope with Barbara's dementia, but I'm not made of stone. This is my sweetheart of over fifty years. I've tried everything to get her to eat and drink and am getting worried because she's losing weight.

She's gone to sleep in the wheelchair again now and as I look at her, I see a shadow of the woman she used to be. The very strong, independent, highly principled Christian woman she was, is no more. She would hate to see herself like this.

Within ten minutes of posting this, I'd received two phone calls from friends who asked what they could do to help. Over the next few hours, I received 187 comments on social media as well as more phone calls than I could count from family and friends offering help. I was truly blessed to have this support, so later that day I added a new post as follows:

Dear All, I'm just overwhelmed by all the comments and phone calls I've received today. Thank you for all your care, concern, and love. I'm truly humbled. Just for the record, Barbara did eat the shepherd's pie. I just wanted to scream this morning!

One of the callers had suggested a food diary for Barbara.

Although I was already doing this as best I could, my main aim was just to get nourishment inside her, so I gave her what I could get her to eat, I wanted her to gain some weight!

I tried to make it as varied as possible and was giving her shepherds pie, cottage pie and fish pie for the main meal, with yogurt and a diced banana for dessert, and a cup of tea.

As we all knew, 2021 was "Olympics" year and the day centre held their own version. When I went to collect Barbara, her carers were excited to tell me that Barbara was now a silver medallist!

I asked what she got the medal for?

"Participation" was the reply. When everyone was singing, Barbara was smiling and laughing, so she was "participating" as best she could.

So, I was now married to an Olympic silver medallist!

Later that week, a long-standing friend from Andover in Hampshire, had invited us to visit for the day. At lunch time, she offered to feed Barbara to give me a break. She ate four or five spoonfuls very slowly and then went to sleep. Was she telling us that she'd had enough, not just of the food, but the whole situation? Who knows?

She had also taken a fancy to chicken curry, Frazzles and onion ring crisps, maybe because of the strong flavour? Quite ironic really as she would limit the amount of crisps our children had when they were growing up, because too many weren't good for you!

Sometimes, I gave her toffee roly-poly for tea. She loved it, again for the sweet taste.

On another day, Barbara didn't eat well. All I could get her to eat all day was:

- half her cornflakes and a cup of tea, then she went to sleep, despite having just had twelve hours of sleep!

- half her Fortisip
- a cup of tea and a biscuit
- a few mouthfuls of chilli con carne (made very small and moist to ease digestion and swallowing)
- apple crumble and custard. She eventually ate it all, but it took ages
- half a cup of tea

Questions and thoughts buzzed through my mind. This isn't enough and no wonder she's losing weight!

- Is she doing this to tell me she's had enough or has she having difficulty swallowing?
- Am I going to watch Barbara die?
- When is this nightmare going to stop?
- Do I want her to die? No.
- Do I want the suffering to stop? Yes, for everybody!

Some days, I felt tired and weary, but we generally walked around Canford Park and watched the children playing on the swings and the roundabout.

One Sunday morning, we went to church as usual. The speaker spoke well and then we had communion. We didn't participate in this as Barbara would go for the big chunk of the loaf rather than the small pieces!

We went home and I gave Barbara a coffee and biscuit. She ate half of the biscuit and then went to sleep. She woke up about twenty minutes later, I gave her the rest of the biscuit then she dozed off again!

I offered her shepherd's pie again for lunch, three spoonfuls and she dozed off again. Every time I gave her food or drink, she would go to sleep! I needed to take her to the toilet and change her, but she was asleep.

When she woke up, I gave her some raspberry jelly that I'd made the day before. I managed to get it down her, so at least there was liquid in her body.

One Monday, two of my old school friends, Russell and Carol, visited. We decided to go to Clevedon for the day and catch up. After a walk along the promenade, we stopped for fish and chips, followed later by a honeycomb ice cream. Unfortunately, Barbara regurgitated the chips and the small bits of fish that I had managed to get into her mouth. Later that day, when we got home, I gave her jam roly-poly for tea! I had to get some food inside her.

A few days later, I started Barbara on a drug called Baclofen to ease the stiffness in her hands and arms. One of our carers also found a pressure sore on Barbara's bottom. I reported it to our GP surgery and the duty doctor referred us to the community nurses.

The next morning, a nurse came just as our carer, Michelle, and I had got Barbara ready. She gave us barrier cream for the sore and said that we'd caught it early, which was a great relief.

Michelle loved Barbara and while we were getting her dressed, she said, "Hey Barb, I want to adopt you as my granny." Looking at me, she added, "Don't get the 'ump Tone, you can be my adopted grandad!" Although we laughed this off as a joke, it was quite an honour and privilege to have someone say that to us.

Later that day, I went to my nephew's wedding, with a friend of mine very kindly offering to look after Barbara for a few hours. I attended the wedding and wedding breakfast and then came home to care for Barbara; I had to get her ready for bed.

After the wedding, Barbara's sister Kath and her son Dave came back with me to see Barbara. She was very sleepy but reacted to her nephew when he started laughing. She started to laugh and then we all joined in. We obviously weren't laughing at the situation, but at the fact that Barbara reacted so positively.

It seemed that Barbara was now surviving on corn flakes, jam roly-poly and custard! The nurse said she had high cholesterol. Not surprising is it on that diet!

Barbara now weighed 7st 8 lb.

While we were washing her that evening, we noticed that she now had spots on her legs and foot. We wondered if it was a reaction to the diet (Frazzles), barrier cream or if it was a circulation problem.

Anyway, we applied some E45 to see if that helped. The next day the spots were worse, so again we queried the cause. We massaged her legs as they were cold and then creamed them again. Barbara seemed to enjoy having her legs massaged.

One night, I had a strange dream. I dreamt about a woman who was laying in the street, naked except for her incontinence pants which were wide open and showed she that had soiled herself. Everyone was looking and passed by horrified. I stopped, picked her up and carried her away to safety.

I woke up startled. It was so vivid.

I immediately compared it to Barbara's situation, although she was not in the street, but being cared for by people that loved her. But it was extremely similar to Barbara's situation. I lay awake for ages just going over and over it in my mind, until eventually falling back to sleep again.

It started me off again, I was overwhelmed with grief. I also felt trapped, there was very little I could do now to change our situation.

The spots on Barbara's legs were going down and I wondered if it had been a reaction to the Baclofen.

3rd September. The sun has got its hat on! Happy Days Memory Café had another cream tea down at the allotment.

Not only did the sun shine (we ordered it especially), but people were glad to see each other again and socialise. One of our carers even watered some of the plants!

We spent time on gardening type activities, planting seeds and making lavender bags etc, which went down well. We followed that with the promised cream tea and silly songs like "If I knew you were coming, I'd have baked a cake", "Papa's got a head like a ping pong ball" and so on. One of the Alive staff went home with the "Papa" song ringing in his ears. I wonder why!

A lovely afternoon.

Ups and Downs – Highs and Lows

The next day was our 56th wedding anniversary, so I took Barbara to Severn Beach for the day. It was lovely.

After church, we went for a walk to Canford Park. It was great, sitting on a bench watching children play, two boys playing football, a family or group of friends playing volleyball and lots of children on the swings in the playground. The sun shone and people were having fun. The simple things of life.

Chicken curry for tea!

Barbara's legs were cold, so I massaged them to try and increase circulation and also put a blanket round them.

Do people with dementia suffer from the cold?

I remembered years ago that Barbara used to complain of being cold all the time, or was this due to poor circulation?

I took her temperature which was 90.8 F. 98.4F is normal, so her temperature was a little bit on the low side. She was also very sleepy, so I let her sleep.

The next morning, her temperature was 94.4F, so I made sure she kept warm. I gave her plenty of drinks, cottage pie for lunch, during which she went to sleep again. We had a quiet day.

On 23rd October, following the normal routine of washing, dressing and breakfast, we decided to watch my favourite programme, the Repair Shop, on TV. Barbara fell asleep, however, halfway through the programme. She woke up anxious and crying. I thought she may be uncomfortable, so I changed her, gave her a cup of tea and a biscuit and paracetamol, in case she had any pain.

However, she was still crying, so I rang my daughter who lived locally. She arrived soon after with her husband and my grandson. He had been on a gap year from university and hadn't seen Barbara for some time. He was quite shocked and upset to see how thin she was.

Soon after my youngest daughter and her husband arrived.

After a bit of discussion and trying to establish why Barbara was crying, we rang 999.

Soon after that Barbara's youngest sister and her husband arrived. After bringing everyone up to date, we prayed together.

Then the paramedics arrived, and we gave them all the background and history. They gave Barbara a thorough check over. We asked if it was a circulation problem. They took her temperature, and the temperature of both legs were the same. Basically, they couldn't find anything. But said they would refer her to our GP to refer her onto a dementia specialist. In the meantime, she should continue taking paracetamol four times a day for 48 hours.

The next day, I got Barbara up and she seemed OK. I gave her cornflakes for breakfast and then the pain relief tablets. Family members and friends rang to see how Barbara was.

It was raining, so we couldn't go to church as Barbara would get soaked. So we watched music videos on YouTube with me singing the songs to her. She always seemed to enjoy this, but after a while, she'd had enough and fell asleep.

On Monday, I rang the GP surgery and spoke to the duty doctor. After explaining what had happened, she said, "Bring her in, I'll see her now." Following an examination of her legs and feet, the doctor referred Barbara to Southmead Hospital's Vascular Department.

I phoned our Navigator to let her know what was going on.

Bristol is unique in the UK, in that people living with dementia are catered for by the Dementia Wellbeing Service (DWS) and both carer and person with dementia are allocated a Navigator who assesses their needs and signposts them to the appropriate specialist.

I wondered again how dementia affected people's senses.

How had it affected Barbara's hearing, sight, smell, taste and sense of pain?

Her hearing seemed OK, she responded to activity around the house and at the day centre. Earlier in her illness, she had cried when she heard an ambulance, police car or fire engine.

Her sight also seemed OK.

Regarding her sense of smell, I wasn't sure whether it was affected or not.

With her taste, she certainly developed a sweet tooth. I tried giving her food that was easily digestible, whether it was savoury or sweet.

Some people believe that people with dementia don't feel pain, but I can vouch for the fact that this isn't true. However, it can be hard to tell if they are in pain. If it is not treated properly, it can cause discomfort and distress.

Please see the useful information and contacts at the end of this book for more information on this theme.

I read an article from the Alzheimers' Society, with which I agree, and which readers may find useful.

"We need person-centred care that runs right through health and social services. Many of the people who are doing care jobs do it because they want to make a difference - but there's not a lot of training, not a lot of development, and not a lot of recognition.

"Things aren't going to change in my lifetime, but we need to start pushing for change now in the hope our children and their children get all the support they need".

James White, Head of Public Affairs and Campaigns, commented:

"We need to see long-term commitment to social care reform, the promised £500m discharge fund to get people out of hospital and into care, and a People Plan to make sure the care workforce is skilled, supported, and sustainable. Only then will care workers be able to do what they do best, providing the kind of high-quality, personalised care people need, to live the lives they want."

"Be the reason someone feels welcome, seen, valued, loved and supported."

Michelle found one of Barbara's pressure sores was open again, so I rang the community nurses. Fortunately, we had some appropriate dressings, which was just as well, because the nurse arrived three days later. After she had changed Barbara's dressing, I took her to the Vascular Department at Southmead Hospital. After tests, I was told that her arteries could cope with pressure stockings if that was required.

For the remainder of the year, we had reviews of Barbara's diet by the Speech & Language Team and regular visits from community nurses to deal with pressure sores.

2022: Dementia Wins

For years, people had been telling me to book some respite. I was reluctant to do this, as it would mean putting Barbara into a care home for a week.

My views on care homes have already been recorded earlier in this book. However, I thought it might be useful to conduct some research, as I had come across a few good care homes through my work with BDAA.

I contacted a couple, but they couldn't cope with Barbara's needs. Eventually I found one that seemed to tick a lot of the boxes on my list, so I phoned the manager to arrange a visit to the home. It was great, staff were very friendly and welcoming and showed me round, pointing out that they had all the necessary equipment to cater for Barbara's needs. It was situated next to a school and pre-school which was ideal for her as a nursery nurse, she could see through the large window and hear the children playing and laughing.

The manager also arranged to meet me at our house. I said that the care home seemed ideal for Barbara and asked if I could I book her in for a week's respite from 7th April.

All plans were set in place with the home being booked and me arranging to visit my daughter in Scotland for a few days and my other daughter in Cornwall for the rest of the week. Quite a lot of travelling involved, but at least I could spend some time with family.

Barbara was still attending the day centre twice a week, but on 18th March they rang to say that they had an outbreak of Covid. I obviously kept Barbara at home, but on the 21st with head throbbing, nose running and a sore throat, I tested positive!

My obvious thought was that Barbara would catch it from me and all the respite plans would fail.

There then followed a series of stressful days in which I had to monitor how Covid was affecting us:

24/03/22	I tested positive.	
30/03/22	I tested negative.	
30/03/22	Barbara tested positive.	During the day she let out two squeals. Was this the effects of Covid on her? I'll never know.
31/03/22	I tested negative	Barbara tested positive.
01/04/22	I tested negative	Barbara tested positive.
03/04/22	Barbara tested negative.	Hooray!
04/04/22	Barbara tested negative.	
05/04/22	Barbara tested negative	Phew! what a relief!
06/04/22	Barbara tested negative for the fourth time. The Care home manager made a visit to finalise arrangements for the respite care tomorrow.	
07/04/22	I took Barbara to the care home.	

Her bedroom was situated opposite the Activity Coordinators' office. This was great because they (two of them) could keep a close eye on her, although it seemed that Barbara spent most of the time asleep as she had at home.

The bedroom was nice, airy, and bright. I unpacked Barbara's clothes and settled her in before she fell asleep. I stayed with her for a while and then decided to go home and pack for my trip to Scotland. I had the same feelings in leaving Barbara at the care home as that time when I had initially dropped her at the day centre all those years ago. It's like taking your child to school for the very first time and leaving them under somebody else's care.

The next day, I travelled by train up to Scotland to see my middle daughter and her family. A nice journey up the east coast of the country.

That evening, I rang the home to see how Barbara was and discovered that she was settled and sleeping a lot of the time, but that the staff were having problems with her eating and drinking. I told them what I had been doing at home under the advice of the

S&L Team and they said that they would try that.

The next day, 9th April, we visited my grandson and his family and had a lovely family day out, culminating in a special evening meal to celebrate my son in law's birthday. I also rang the home to see how things were going and see if staff were still having problems with Barbara's eating and drinking.

The following day, we took the family to a local country park which was an opportunity to spoil the grandchildren! After all, the purpose of a grandparent is to spoil their grandchildren, isn't it? It was a lovely day.

Once again, I rang the home and staff were still having problems with Barbara's eating and drinking.

On 11th April (my Mum's birthday – she would have been 106 if she was still alive), I travelled back to Bristol but had to go via London. A long day, but I called in for a chicken chow mein on the way home from the station, to save me cooking a meal at home.

Barbara was still not eating and drinking properly, and I arranged to visit the home the next morning.

When I arrived, Barbara was asleep, looking very peaceful and relaxed; she didn't seem to be in pain at all. I had a discussion with the staff and team about the situation.

Were we now entering the final phase?

The senior nurse asked, "What are your plans now, you're having respite aren't you?"

I said "Yes, I've been to see my daughter and her family in Scotland, now I'm planning to see my youngest daughter's family in Cornwall for a couple of days."

She replied, "Go and see your daughter, don't worry about Barbara, we'll look after her. Go and be her husband rather than her carer for a while."

So, I got the train to Cornwall, met with my daughter and family and brought everyone up to date.

That evening I spoke to my eldest daughter and son on the phone. They had both visited Barbara whilst I was travelling south that afternoon. I asked them what they thought about the situation. They both agreed that Barbara seemed to be quite restful and at peace, and that she should stay there permanently. She now needed to be cared for by professionals, I had done my bit. I said that I needed to check that there was a room at the care home first, then came the issue of who pays?

We all agreed that, maybe now, Barbara felt that she could "let go" at last. She been fighting this awful condition for over twenty years and put up one heck of a fight!

The next morning, my youngest daughter, Ruth, and I went to a local café/restaurant for a late breakfast and then I travelled back to Bristol that afternoon.

I contacted Care Direct the next morning about the situation and we discussed finances. In the circumstances we were in, the process was that, following an assessment, Bristol City Council would pay for care for the first twelve weeks, then it was down to me to pay. Following this discussion, I sent an email to our allocated social worker, saying that we were extending respite for another week whilst I confirmed there was a place for Barbara at the home, an assessment would be undertaken, and a finance package arranged.

After this, I went to the care home as it was the end of the first week's respite. Barbara was asleep on my arrival, so I had a chat with the manager and asked how things were. I told her what our thoughts were as a family, and asked if there was a vacant room that Barbara could have. She replied that there was. First hurdle over!

I went in to see Barbara. She was asleep, but as I walked into the room, her eyes opened, and I kissed her and held her hand. Her eyes told me that she recognised me. She may not have been able to communicate verbally, but she communicated through her smile.

I stayed with her for some time. Carers and nurses popped in to see how we were, tea and biscuits were brought in every so often, and both of us were treated like royalty. The staff were amazing.

Eventually the time came for me to leave. Barbara wasn't eating or drinking very much, even when I tried feeding her, and she kept falling asleep every so often. As I left, I said to the staff that I was leaving now and asked them to look after and take good care of "my Barb". I didn't really have to tell them that, as they all seemed to love her.

At home that evening, I felt very lonely as the bed and hoist were there, but Barbara wasn't. It seemed strange to watch TV with Barbara's bed now empty. Obviously, there had been no conversation, but at least she was there before.

All sorts of questions had been going through my mind.

- Had I been doing the wrong things for the right reasons?
- Could I have done more to help Barbara?
- Could I have acted earlier?
- Was I right in having respite?
- Had Barbara got worse because I'd changed her routine?

Like a lot of carers, I was feeling guilty and asking myself if I was doing enough.

Carers I've spoken to over the years have said that they have often asked themselves those same questions, but we are human beings, and we do what we can in good faith, hoping that we're helping.

The following day, Dilys (my daughter's mother-in-law and a friend) and I went to the care home to see Barbara. She was asleep and hadn't eaten very much.

I felt so helpless, there was nothing I could do except hold her hand, tell her I love her and that she's still my best girl and always will be.

On Saturday I went to the care home again, there was still no change. I hate this disease.

Sunday was Easter Sunday. A great service at church led by James the minister, involving the children making Easter gardens. Lots of folk asking how Barbara was, and how I was coping. People are very kind, aren't they?

I visited Barbara with Dilys in the afternoon and I demonstrated how we feed Barbara to more staff, but she didn't respond as normal to the chocolate custard we offered her. She was getting thinner in the face and had hardly had any cheeks.

On Easter Monday, with some care home staff on leave, I decided not to visit the home.

The following day, our social worker rang to say that if I left Barbara in the care home and she went from "respite care" straight to "nursing care", the council could be fined.

I thought this was unbelievable, so I said, "Excuse me, can you say that again?"

He repeated what he'd just said.

I replied, "That's ridiculous! Why will the council be fined?"

He gave some explanation which I didn't understand then, and still don't!

So, I said, "You're telling me that I've got to bring Barbara home otherwise the council could be fined. That's not only stupid, but it's also unsettling and cruel."

He reiterated the process.

I rang the care agency (who provided my home carers) and asked them to put the carer rota back in place because of what the social worker had told me, that there was a big problem and I had to bring Barbara home. They agreed with me that it was ridiculous and cruel and suggested I do three things:

- Contact our Navigator at the Dementia Wellbeing Service.
- Contact our GP.
- A CHC assessment checklist must be completed either by the community nurses or care home. I could ask the care home easily because she was currently there.

I rang our Navigator and GP and then the care home manager. She said that she could complete the CHC checklist; so I arranged to pick Barbara up on Friday to bring her home.

I was watching my wife and best friend gradually die. We were entering the final phase.

I thought about the importance of support groups. I considered myself fortunate to have support from our family, church, friends, care professionals and the BDAA team. Some carers have nothing.

Their nearest relative might live hundreds of miles away and they might not care anyway!

On Wednesday, a call from Care Direct's finance department confirmed that Barbara's finance request had been registered. I thanked the lady and told her about the struggle I was having with the social worker and that I hoped it would be sorted out soon.

Why doesn't the NHS cover dementia care?

It's regarded as a mental condition, but (in my opinion) it's a physical condition (a disease of the brain) with mental health implications.

I also updated the care agency on what I had done.

Barbara's youngest sister and her husband came to see her at the care home. Needless to say, both were really saddened and upset when they saw how Barbara had deteriorated. I updated them on what was going on and they were horrified to hear about the situation.

That evening we contacted all our family, friends, minister and people at church, professionals, in fact everyone, to pray that common sense would prevail.

The following morning, the social worker rang to say that Barbara could stay at the care home! Hooray, what a relief, miracles do happen!

He also confirmed that she qualified for financial support, with the council paying most of the fee and me topping it up.

Then he hit me with another body blow.

He would conduct a capacity test over Zoom on Monday to check that this was OK with Barbara. I told him that she had been mute for three years, had dementia and was at End of Life. How could she respond to a Zoom call?

I also had Power of Attorney.

He replied he had to do it; it was the process.

I couldn't believe what I was hearing, this was just plain stupidity! Did this guy have any common sense or compassion?

I later visited the home with a friend, Linda from church, who was a big fan of Barbara's and used to enjoy a hug. I wanted to let the care home manager know the news. She confirmed that she had completed the CHC Assessment checklist, so that part of the process was complete. She was horrified to hear that the social worker wanted to do a capacity test over Zoom.

Linda and I spent some time with Barbara, holding her hand, but she slept most of the time.

On Friday 22nd April, I again visited the home.

Barbara looked all skin and bone, but I managed to get her to eat a few spoonfuls of yoghurt and she did swallow them.

The care home manager said that they would arrange Barbara's fourth Covid jab and send off the respite contract. I gave her copies of the Power of Attorney forms and financial contract. I also sent them to the social worker.

At 4am on Monday 25th April, the phone rang. It was the nurse on night duty at the home, ringing to say that Barbara's breathing had changed. "This is it," I thought. "We're at end of life." I got washed and dressed and then went immediately to the care home, informing my children on the way.

On arrival, I was taken in to see Barbara. Her breathing had changed and she was now on palliative care.

Soon after, the family arrived, and we gathered around the bed and took it in turns to hold Barbara's hand and stroke her cheeks (what remained of them) and tell her we loved her.

The staff were lovely again, treating us like royalty, offering us tea and biscuits and even breakfast and later, lunch. The senior nurse came in and we discussed Barbara's situation, and we asked if it was now just a matter of time before she passed away. She said that she could possibly go on like this for a few days, but it would probably be two or three.

We spent the morning sharing stories and memories.

At 2pm a nurse came in with her phone as the social worker had set up the Zoom call to conduct the capacity test with Barbara. The nurse had already told him that, under the circumstances, this was totally inappropriate.

He said that he had to see Barbara and ask her one question: Did she agree to the plans we had made for her?

How could she answer?

I also told him that this was taking human rights too far and totally inappropriate, but to get on with it.

The nurse held the mobile up so that he could see Barbara and asked his question.

We couldn't believe what we were witnessing, we were horrified at the stupidity of what was happening before our very eyes. It felt like this politically correct nonsense was just that, nonsense! Whilst asking his question, Barbara may well have taken her last breath.

The call ended and my eldest daughter then took the phone and spoke to the social worker to express her and our disgust at this process (well basically gave him a piece of her mind!). Particularly as I had Power of Attorney and we had set up it up several years ago and Social Services knew about this because I'd sent them a copy.

We spent the rest of the afternoon with Barbara, kissed her goodbye and then went home.

***

The next day, Tuesday 26th, we again visited the home and took turns in holding Barbara's hand, giving her a soft kiss on the forehead, and telling her how much we loved her.

I remembered those early days years ago, when I would tell Barbara that I loved her, and she would say "I love you too." I would say "How much do you love me?" She would reply, "I love you seven", because seven was a big number. So, over the years, we would always say "I love you seven." Silly really, but you are silly sometimes when you're in love with someone aren't you? Love is really all that matters. We enter this world in love, we depart it in love.

It's not about money, wealth, prestige, how big your car or house is, the most important thing in life is to love and be loved. Sadly, some get their priorities wrong.

Barbara gradually faded and passed away at 5.30pm.

We cried and hugged. Her pain and anguish were over. It was finished. She was at peace now.

To everything there is a season,
a time for every purpose under heaven.
a time to be born, and a time to die. . .
a time to weep, and a time to laugh.
a time to mourn, and a time to dance.
Ecclesiastes 3

My eldest daughter said that I shouldn't spend that night alone and told me I was staying at her house overnight.

A Celebration of Barbara's life

On Wednesday, I spent the morning on the phone, telling people of Barbara's passing away. I also rang the Brain Centre at Southmead Hospital in Bristol to arrange the donation of her brain to the centre for research. We had 72 hours from time of death to get it to the centre. We put the process in motion.

As a family, we had decided years ago that Barbara's brain would be donated in this way, it was what she would have wanted. 50 years ago, when our eldest daughter had died of Leukaemia when aged just six. We had donated her body to help others, so we were carrying out what Barbara would have intended.

Over the next few days, we had some family time and started to arrange the funeral. We didn't want to use the word "funeral", because we wanted to celebrate Barbara's life, so we arranged a "celebration service", well two really, one at Canford Crematorium and the other at Westbury Baptist Church. We had also decided years ago as a family, that we would ask people to wear bright colours, not black, because through her life, Barbara had brought a little colour into people's lives.

Due to Covid and the number of deaths resulting from it, plus work at the crematorium itself, the funeral couldn't take place until 30th May, five weeks away.

Laura from the Brain Centre rang later to say that they had received Barbara's brain in time and that they would therefore be able to give me an accurate diagnosis within six weeks. Because she had the condition for over 20 years, researchers could establish and confirm lots of useful information.

My daughter Ruth and her husband Shayne came with me to arrange the funeral. I said that I wanted my son and five grandsons to be the pallbearers. The funeral directors were happy with that, but they would have to be outside the funeral parlour early to have a little bit of training on how to hold the coffin. It wouldn't weigh very much as Barbara had lost so much weight.

Sheila, our minister, would lead the service at the crematorium and the family would lead the celebration at church afterwards. Flowers would be from our family only and donations of money would be given to BDAA.

That evening, I wrote a letter to Social Services (see Appendix 2) concerning the attitude of our social worker in conducting a capacity test at end of life.

I didn't meet the Social Services Director until August over Zoom. Apparently, my letter had been posted to the wrong address which had caused some delay. The outcome was that the practitioner and his manager had been interviewed to review and discuss the decisions and actions that were taken. Appropriate action and training had taken place with the whole team to prevent this happening to other families.

The team also "would like to extend their most sincere apologies for the distress caused to you and your family at such a difficult time."

So, if lessons were learnt and processes/procedures changed, that's fine.

Due to the delayed funeral, we were now in a state of limbo really.

Our family, friends and neighbours were very kind to me over the next few weeks and invited me out for pub lunches, barbecues, and other meals, so my social life exploded and hit the roof!

I had also thought about having a memorial bench made for Barbara, but where would I place it? We had often gone to Clevedon when we had a problem to resolve. Barbara and I would walk along the promenade chewing the cud, around Poets Walk and back across the green to the promenade again and on to the pub by the pier. We would have a meal on the upstairs terrace overlooking the Bristol Channel towards Wales and watch the sunset. Lovely! Problem solved, or at least a possible way forward.

Dilys and I took a trip down there to check out a potential site for a bench and noted a couple of good positions.

Another possibility was Canford Park in Westbury on Trym. We often used to walk there and took the grandchildren when they were small. During Covid lockdowns, I had often walked Barbara around there in her wheelchair as our daily walk.

On 9th May, the hospital bed and hoist were removed, and I started to tidy up the house.

That evening, BDAA trustees suggested we close the office for two weeks.

I started to tidy the house again in an attempt to restore it back to a family home. I took the wheelchair back to the centre at Patchway and gave nightdresses/pants to the care home, where they could make good use of them.

However, the house had no atmosphere anymore, it seemed dead.

In May, I did a longstanding dementia awareness session at St. Peter's Hospice. BDAA were called in to run six sessions a year for staff and volunteers, plus it had a slot at their "End of Life" training day. I could do it from experience now.

I was feeling very lonely, the house seemed very empty. The bed and hoist had gone, the wheelchair had been returned and the supply of incontinence pants had been given away.

Should I start going through Barbara's clothes and belongings? I decided not to, it was too early. Everything I picked up or looked at brought back a memory, some good, some not so good.

What really worried me was that I couldn't cry! I had just lost my best friend and I couldn't cry.

Why?

Was I so desensitised that I couldn't cry any more, or was it that I had no tears left after caring for her for twenty odd years?

Later that morning I went to have my second Covid booster. When the pharmacist had done that, he asked if I would like to have my blood pressure tested. I said, "Yes please."

When he took the reading, his eyebrows rose, and he looked

at me with a concerned look. It was high at 200/107. Normally it would be approximately 155/90. He asked if I generally had high blood pressure or took any medication for it. I replied that over the years, my blood pressure was high, but that I controlled it through diet and exercise. I told him that my wife had just passed away and was that was probably the cause. He said that maybe the stress would contribute to the high reading, but to visit my GP immediately.

There was no way to get a GP appointment immediately, so I went home and relaxed for the rest of the day. Readings taken later showed that my blood pressure had fallen.

The next day, Friday, my blood pressures had fallen further, but I went out for a walk to get some exercise.

Later that morning, our retired minister, Sheila, came to visit me regarding the order of service at Canford Crematorium. It was Sheila who had asked Barbara to get involved in WotsTots years before and they had always got on well.

I told her that attendees had been asked to wear bright colours and not black. Barbara had brought colour to those she met, and we wanted to celebrate that rather than be mournful. We wanted the service to be full of celebratory songs, poems and contributions from our family. I did think of having "More than a woman" as one of the songs, as it was our song, but decided to choose others, because it was about all of us celebrating Barbara's life, not just me. I used to sing this song to her and we would dance to it.

We were also planning to have a celebration at our church along the same pattern.

We all still missed her of course, but we wanted to celebrate her life. Over the next couple of weeks, we arranged the crematorium service and the celebration at church and ordered the family flowers. We ordered some lily of the valley, Barbara's favourite. I had a "moment" when completing the card.

Monday 30th May arrived, "The Day", the celebration of Barbara's life!

The family would travel from the funeral parlour in Westbury

Village to Canford Crematorium, about half a mile, in one hearse and some family cars.

As we walked from home to the village, I saw six very smart chaps in sharp suits and thought the Bristol Mafia were in town! Then I realised it was my son and grandsons who had arrived for their little bit of training with Barbara's coffin.

We arrived at the crematorium to find it packed with people, it was standing room only with the front couple of rows reserved for the family. I was really choked up to think that Barbara had been part of the lives of so many people.

My bit in the service was just to say a prayer. The obituary would take place later at the church service. I had written it down just in case I stumbled. It read:

> Thank you, God, for giving Barbara to me sixty years ago as an answer to prayer.
>
> Thank you for the honour and privilege of being her husband for fifty-seven years.
>
> She has battled this awful disease of dementia for the last twenty years and going into the care home those few days has allowed her finally to rest, be out of pain and be at peace.
>
> Her work with us is complete; she has had a positive effect on the lives of so many people, both young and older.
>
> Now she needs to go home to you, please take her to be with yourself as you promised and please take care of her.
>
> Thank you for loaning her to me for all these years. She will always be my best friend, sweetheart and my best girl. I will always love her.

Sheila gave a very splendid tribute to Barbara, a much-loved woman, during her address. Then we filed out to the Garden of Remembrance

We couldn't stay long, we had to be at church for the Celebration Service.

This was led by my oldest daughter, with lots of our family and friends taking part. Our family are a motley crew, but they're ours, and we love them all. The service lasted nearly two hours, but again, apart from the row behind the family, it was standing room only with more chairs being brought in.

Barbara was our rock and this attendance proved how loved and respected she was by everybody.

We were also absolutely amazed that over £2000 was donated to BDAA in Barbara's memory.

I want to say that life returned to normal after the funeral, but of course, it could never return to normal, Barbara wasn't there anymore. Like a lot of widows or widowers, I grieved by throwing myself into work and so I spent most of my time on BDAA business.

A month had now gone by since Barbara's funeral. How did I feel?

Up and down really, I had good days and bad days.

Difficult writing my daughter's birthday card this month, writing "from Dad", not "Mum and Dad".

One morning, I decided to have eggs for breakfast and remembered the time I cracked two eggs for breakfast which made Barbara laugh. It was easy to make her laugh, and she had a lovely smile which melted everybody's hearts. Memories occur all the time.

Another day, Sunday, I felt lonely and depressed. I missed Barbara; life seemed pointless without her. We were a good team together.

A (lady) friend sitting by me in church that day must have sensed my feelings and held my arm as we sang a hymn. Was God comforting me through her?

I walked the familiar walk through Canford Park after church, the one I used to walk with Barbara. I would place Barbara's memorial bench in front of the children's playground, she would love that.

Barbara had symptoms of dementia for 20 years or more, as it probably started when she was in her fifties. So, she had early or young onset dementia and I read that today there are 70,800 people with young onset dementia (YOD) in the UK. 70% are men.

Of the 5000 people with dementia in Bristol, 1000 have YOD.

We do need to provide support and activity for these folk!

On Christmas Eve, I took a walk up to The Downs, a walk down "Memory Lane" as Barbara and I would often go there.

Middle aged and older couples were strolling along hand in hand or arm in arm. Nice. Make the most of it, I thought, you never know what tomorrow will bring. I remember Barbara and I walking hand in hand to the sea wall, where, in summer, we would buy an ice-cream and sit on a bench and enjoy being out together. Touch has so much importance in life, doesn't it? I think one of the lessons we learned from Covid it how important touch is. When someone hugs you, the warmth and good feeling you get is immeasurable. I missed that now that Barbara was not here anymore.

Nice to see young lovers taking photos of each other at the sea wall and laughing at the results.

It was great to see families with young children out having a pre-Christmas bit of fresh air. Parents taking their kids out to use up some of their energy, so that they would sleep that night. Children tempering their excitement as "the man in the big red suit" would arrive in just a few hours. I know it's a made-up story based on St Nicholas, but it's a bit of fun isn't it and stimulates a child's imagination and curiosity. We all know Christmas is really all about the birth of a baby, one that would change the world.

2023: A Year of Anniversaries

Christmas and New Year were difficult for me. Barbara would normally be busy cooking and preparing for the family to come together. Although we met as family, she was not there.

Our panto at Happy Days was Snow White and the Seven Dwarfs this year. I wondered how they would cope with this, as there were only three actors! It all worked out OK though, with the actors disappearing behind a screen and coming out again a few minutes later as a different character, so it was an interesting afternoon.

I woke up one morning and it was a wet start to the day, but at lunchtime the rain stopped. I thought I'd take a walk for some exercise; I was trying to walk an hour a day.

I'm a strong believer in "use it or lose it".

As I went out of the front door, the sun came out. Lovely.

I walked a circular walk that I used to walk Barbara round in her wheelchair. Another walk down "Memory Lane"! I finished up in Canford Park where I had placed her memorial bench in front of the children's playground. The bench was empty, so I sat on it and looked at her memorial plaque.

It may seem silly, but I said, "Afternoon Barb" and started to talk to her. I knew she wasn't physically there, but like a lot of people who grieve for a loved one, I did the same, I talked to her. The sun came out again; was this a sign that she'd heard me? Your imagination runs riot. It did bring some comfort, even though it seemed to be a one-way conversation. I told her how much I missed her and that I loved her more than words can say.

I missed her because we were a team and I'm a great believer in teams, as my BDAA team will confirm. Barbara would keep me grounded. I would come up with all sorts of mad ideas and she would say, "You can't do that."

I would reply, "Why not?"

We would then have a conversation and come up with something that was practical and sensible. I missed that. I missed her smile, her touch, I missed her hugs, I missed holding her, feeling the warmth of her body against me. I missed her.

It's quite ironic, but as I write these words today, the song "Want you back for good" by Take That is playing in the background. It sums up my feeling.

Most of the time I'm fine, particularly when I'm busy, but then these feelings suddenly come over me like waves.

Then there was a different day, I took my grandson Jacob home to Cornwall, so that he could spend some time with his mum and dad (and so could I).

Good Friday came and was a difficult day. As I've mentioned before, it had special significance for me on two counts. Not only is it the day the world remembers that Jesus died, but it is also the day our daughter Janice died. A third element this year was that 7th April was when my Mum died, just a short time before her 84th birthday on 11th April.

Easter Sunday arrived, Resurrection Day to Christians, with Barbara and I being believers. Living with the pain of not having her with me is temporary however, I will see her again. She has been reunited with our Lord and our daughter Janice and one day, I will be with both of them too.

With Barbara's first anniversary of passing away on the 26th, April was a sad month for me. My family asked me what I was going to do on Barbara's anniversary.

"I'm going to have the day off," I said, "and go to Clevedon, walk along the promenade, around the headland to "Poets Walk", back across the large field where the steam train is, back along the promenade to the pub by the pier. There, I will book an upstairs table on the terrace overlooking the channel towards Wales and watch the sunset." Sounds quite romantic, doesn't it?

Barbara and I used to do this when we had a problem to resolve or just a day out.

One of my children asked if I was going to do this on my own. I said "I'll do the walk on my own, but if you would all like to join me for the meal, that would be good and that way we can all remember Mum." So, those that were able, joined me on the meal, but we all remembered Barbara in our own way.

30th May was the first anniversary of Barbara's funeral and celebration of her life service. We had received lots of positive feedback from the people that had attended either or both occasions. Some had only known Barbara with dementia and were quite surprised to realise how active she had been in the past.

2nd June was Barbara's birthday. She would have been 76. I decided to put a bunch of red roses on her bench in Canford Park. I miss her terribly, but she is still my girl.

***

What now?

Thank you for reading this book. I hope it has helped you to understand one couple's journey with dementia. If it helps you on your journey with dementia, then that's even better. That is why I wrote it.

Living with someone who has dementia is hard, both physically and emotionally. It demands a lot of patience, in fact "A Bucketful of Patience".

Please, also feel free to contact me on chair@bdaa.org.uk
Tony

Letter to Care Home Manager **Appendix 1**

Dear (Manager),

I just thought I would write a few thoughts down in a letter regarding how I received Barbara back last Saturday afternoon when I collected her.

Trying to gain access to the home is really difficult as a visitor, unless someone is on Reception or near the front door. Once I did gain access, I was asked if I knew the front door code! As a visitor, I shouldn't know the front door code, should I? So, the question is, "Does your security policy need reviewing?"

When I did get into the home, I was taken up to see where Barbara was and she was in the communal room, where the TV is. When I saw Barbara, my heart sank. She looked ten or twenty years older than she is, because her hair (which has always been her pride and joy) was combed straight back with no style. Surely someone can comb her hair properly. This is basic care.

When we went to Barbara's room, the nurse took the case from on top of the wardrobe, where I put it a week ago, and put it on the bed. She then started to take Barbara's clean and unused clothes and just threw them in the case. No care about folding them neatly and putting them in. I got the impression she just wanted to get rid of us as quickly as possible.

Some of Barbara's clothes were still in laundry, which is fair enough. She is incontinent and therefore subject to a change of clothes or two during the day. However, on arrival, an inventory was made regarding the clothes Barbara arrived with. No such check on the inventory on departure was made. Neither has there been any follow up contact with us to say "We have a pair of Barbara's trousers or nightdress here" etc. and arrange a pickup. I do realise that Barbara's things weren't labelled and that is down to me, however, can I come and collect the remainder of Barbara's things and return some stuff that doesn't belong to her.

As we were packing, the nurse asked if I would like to have some feedback from the nurse looking after Barbara, I said that I would and was introduced to a man who was going around giving folk their medication. Fair enough, people need their medication on time, but I needed to know how Barbara had been during the week. All he said was that Barbara had settled down and was calm.

When we had finished packing, I took Barbara to say "Goodbye "and went round the top floor to do that. I asked the nurse if there was any booking out process. She said "No, if you've packed your case, you can go".

Nobody showed us to the door or saw us off the property, whereas it was all smiles and welcome on arrival. The attitude seemed to be that we've had your money, now clear off. Lack of basic customer care.

When I got Barbara home, I took her to the toilet. As you know she is incontinent and prone to regular trips to the toilet and change of "pull-ups". When I undressed her, she was wearing a pair of knickers with a pad and she was soaking wet, really soaking wet. Now, she may have wet herself on the way home or she may have been wet when I picked her up, I'll never know. Why wasn't she wearing the pull-ups I'd provided? More importantly however, was that she was red raw between her legs due to urine, or what I call "Nappy-rash". I had brought Sudocrem from home to prevent this, as I apply it when I shower her.

I decided to give her a shower and found that her fingernails were black and full of dirt – it looked as if she had been gardening all afternoon. Also, she wasn't wearing a bra! I have to ask, "Who dressed and showered her that morning?" This again is basic care.

When I brought Barbara on the arrival Friday, I was asked for Barbara's repeat prescription in case she needed medication. I haven't been given it back.

Before arrival, Barbara had been given an initial assessment, on arrival an inventory was made of her possessions. No final assessment or feedback has been organised. When visiting on the Tuesday evening, my son was told that someone, a resident, had threatened to smack Barbara if she tried to hug her. This person obviously has no understanding of dementia or may have the condition themselves, but the question is "What is your anti-violence policy or vulnerable person policy?" What's your strategy for dealing with situations like this?

Most of this happened at a weekend when you may have had minimum staffing, but would you leave a loved one in the care of a "Care Home" like this. I've lost confidence in those who work at your care home and ask that you cancel the provisional booking I made for three weeks in Feb/ Mar 2017.

I'll bring back the things that don't belong to Barbara, collect my prescription and the rest of Barbara's things and if you would like to have a discussion about the above, that's fine.

Letter to Social Services — Appendix 2

Dear Sir/Madam,

I am writing to you following the transfer to nursing care from respite care for my wife Barbara over the last couple of weeks.

To give you the context, the timing of events was as follows:

1. I have been caring for my wife Barbara, who has Frontal Temporal Dementia, since 1999.
2. I have been encouraged to have respite care for some time and on 7th April 2022, I booked her into a care home for a week's respite.
3. Whilst at the care home, staff reported that they were having real problems getting her to eat and drink. (We have had this issue for 15 – 18 months and been following the advice of the S< Team, which was shared with staff.)
4. My daughter and son visited Barbara and we all agreed that she now had reached the stage where she needed to have nursing care in a care home rather than at our family home.
5. I booked Barbara in for another week's respite (which would end on 21st April)
6. This extra week's respite would give me time to enquire about and arrange nursing care.
7. An Assessment and Income Officer assessed Barbara's financial assets and wrote to say that Barbara would not have to pay.
8. When I spoke to one of your social workers, he told me that he would have to check with his manager if Barbara could go from respite care to nursing care immediately, as Bristol City Council could be fined if this happened.
   I asked "Why?".
   I still don't understand the answer, so I asked if that meant I had to remove Barbara from the care home and take her home.
   "Yes" was the reply.
   I said that this was ridiculous, not only that, but it was also cruel to take a frail, mute woman with Dementia at "End of Life" out of the care home.
9. Following pressure from various professionals aware of Barbara and her illness, common sense eventually prevailed, and I was told that Barbara could stay in the care home.
10. The social worker said that he would conduct a capacity test over

Zoom on Monday to check that this was OK with Barbara.
I told him that she had been mute for three years, had dementia and was at End of Life, how could she take part in a Zoom call.
I also had Power of Attorney, which had been copied to Care Direct.
He replied he had to do it, it was the process!

11. At 04.00. on Monday 25th April, I received a call from the nurse on night duty at the home reporting that Barbara's breathing had changed.
12. I went immediately to the care home and informed my children.
13. At 14.00. a nurse came in with her phone as the social worker had set up the Zoom call to conduct the capacity test.
14. The nurse had already told him this was inappropriate under the circumstances.
15. He said that he had to see Barbara and ask her one question.
16. I also told him that this was not appropriate, but to get on with it.
17. The nurse held the mobile up so that he could see Barbara and asked his question.
18. We were/are all horrified at this! Whilst asking her his question, Barbara may well have taken her last breath!
19. My daughter then spoke to the social worker to express her, and our, disgust at this process, particularly as I had Power of Attorney.
20. We had set up Power of Attorney several years ago and Social Services knew about this.

What would you do if it was your loved one?
I have been advised to go to the media with this incident, however may I suggest you have an urgent review of this process? It was either written by someone:

1. who had never experienced End of Life with a loved one.
2. without an ounce of compassion in their soul.
3. with a view of potential litigation (i.e. fear) rather than common sense (which isn't so common these days!)

Please don't send me your apologies, they're just empty words and the standard, political response, we ask for change to prevent other people at EOL to go through this same process.

Yours sincerely
Tony Hall

Some useful contacts

Alzheimer's Society
Web: www.alzheimers.org.uk
alzheimerssocietyuk
Tel: 0117 961 0693
Helpline: 0333 150 3456
@alzheimerssoc

Bristol Dementia Action Alliance (BDAA)
Web: www.bdaa.org.uk
BristolDAA
Tel: 07849 403018
@BristolDAA

Bristol Dementia Wellbeing Service (DWS)
Web www.bristoldementiawellbeing.org
BristolDWS
Tel: 0117 904 5151
Helpline: 0333 150 3456
@BristolDWS

Dementia UK
Web: www.dementiauk
Helpline: 0800 888 6678

Purple Angel Global
Web: purpleangel-global.com

Some useful books and further reading

Somebody I used to know	Wendy Mitchell
Losing Clive to Younger Onset Dementia	Helen Beaumont
50+ Shades of Dementia!	Norrms McNamara
Knickers in the Fridge	Jane Grierson
Contented Dementia	Oliver James
The Dementia Guide	Alzheimer's Society

Some useful tips (author unknown)

1.	Agree	never argue
2.	Divert	never reason
3.	Distract	never shame
4.	Reassure	never lecture
5.	Reminisce	never say "remember"
6.	Repeat	never say "I told you"
7.	Let them do what they can do	never say "you can't"
8.	Ask	never demand
9.	Encourage	never condescend
10.	Reinforce	never force